Adventures in Other Lands

Speed and Comprehension Reader

Matilda Nordtvedt

A Beka Book® Pensacola, FL 32523-9100
a ministry of PENSACOLA CHRISTIAN COLLEGE

Speed and Comprehension Readers

Adventures in Other Lands
Adventures in Nature
Adventures in Greatness

Adventures in Other Lands: Speed and Comprehension Reader

Staff Credits

Editors: Marion Hedquist, Heidi Mayfield

Designer: John Ball

Illustrators: Jason Atwell, Bill Bailey, John Ball, Kyle Henry

A Beka Book, a Christian textbook ministry of Pensacola Christian College, is designed to meet the need for Christian textbooks and teaching aids. The purpose of this publishing ministry is to help Christian schools reach children and young people for the Lord and train them in the Christian way of life.

Illustration on page 1 based on images from Digital Stock Corporation.

Cataloging Data
Nordtvedt, Matilda.
Adventures in other lands: speed and comprehension reader / Matilda Nordtvedt.
p. : ill.; 23 cm.—(A Beka Book reading program)
1. Reading comprehension—Study and teaching (Elementary)
2. Reading (Elementary)
Library of Congress: PE1119 .N67 A28 1998
Dewey System: 428.6

To Parents and Teachers

Adventures in Other Lands is a speed and comprehension reader, correlated with the *A Beka Book* Fourth Grade Reading Curriculum.

In fourth grade, the reading program provides specific opportunities for students to develop their comprehension skills. At this level, students have become personally responsible for much more history and science material and outside reading. Their vocabulary work is increased and they are expected to retain many more facts. Now is the time to begin stressing the importance of reading for information at the best possible speed. Because the reading program for the lower elementary grades stresses phonics and reading mastery, students are now ready to begin working on these other reading skills.

The best way to help students develop these skills is to allow time for much practice and to provide them with a variety of stimulating, well-written reading materials. The ability to comprehend is really the ability to *concentrate.* Teach your students good habits that will help them to concentrate.

It is not helpful to turn the development of comprehension skills into a "science" by spending the reading class finding core parts of the sentence, analyzing patterns of paragraph organization, recognizing related thought groups, etc. This is unnecessary if you have the right kind of language arts program. Spend the reading class reading!

The speed and comprehension exercises for grades 4–6 are purposely varied as to content, degree of difficulty, and length. They are challenging and interesting. Quizzes are included for each reading exercise. Each question has a 10 point value. Subtract the total from 100 to get the grade. Further instructions are included in the day-by-day lesson plans available in the Grade Four Reading Curriculum.

To the Student

The selections in this book are written about countries around the world, children who have lived there, and the missionaries God called there to teach the people about Jesus. As you read the stories of these missionaries, you will discover that they have lived lives of great adventure—and sometimes great danger. They have also lived lives of great blessing. And the children who have grown up in these faraway places, whether they were living on the street in the Philippines, lost in the jungles of Peru, or running for their life in Africa, faced the same questions that you face almost every day: What do I do when I'm scared? What do I do when everything goes wrong? Who can I turn to? Can I really trust the Lord to take care of me? How blessed we are to have churches in America where we can hear the truth. Perhaps the Lord wants you to share the truth with children in other lands who haven't heard it yet.

Pronunciation Key

Symbol	Example
ā	āte
â	dâre
ă	făt
ä	fäther
ə	ago (ə·gō′)
ch	chin
ē	ēven
ĕ	ĕgg
*ẽ (ər)	pondẽr
g	good
ī	īce
ĭ	ĭt
j	jog
ks	perplex (ks = x)
kw	quart (kw = qu)
ng	song
ō	ōver

Symbol	Example
ô	côrd, taught, saw
ŏ	nŏt
oi	boil
o͞o	bro͞od
o͝o	bo͝ok
ou	out
sh	shark
th	thin
t̶h̶	t̶h̶ere
*tū̑ (cho͞o)	virtū̑e
ū	ūnit
û	ûrn
ŭ	ŭp
zh	azure (zh = z)
’	little (lĭt′’l; shows that the vowel is not sounded)

***Note:** For simplicity, the alternate symbols are used for ẽr and tū̑.

Contents

God Was Taking Care of Andre

Note these words:
Andre (än′drā) Dwina (dwīn′ə) Chad (chăd)

Andre Dwina lives in Chad, Africa. When missionaries came to his area, he was one of the first to believe in Jesus. After he became a Christian he told everyone he met about his Savior and the hope He had given him.

Andre had the opportunity to attend short-term Bible schools taught by the missionaries who had come from the United States. He became a lay evangelist, which means he went about preaching even if he had little education to do so.

One day Andre decided to go to a neighboring village to preach. He told no one where he was going. That was good, because the next day when soldiers came to arrest him, nobody could tell them where Andre had gone.

When the soldiers finally found out, Andre had left that village for another one. For about three weeks the soldiers followed Andre from one village to another.

Andre preached in all these villages, but the people did not listen to him. "You are a hunted man," they said, "as good as dead."

Finally the soldiers caught up to Andre and arrested him. They stripped him of his clothes, tied him up, and beat him. They threatened him with death if he would not deny Jesus. When Andre refused to do so, they picked a day to execute him.

When the day of his execution came, none of the soldiers wanted to pull the trigger on this unusual man. They decided to bury him alive instead. They had killed other Christians this way before.

Andre was forced to dig his own grave. He was then put into it to be buried alive, but the soldiers could not bring themselves to cover him with dirt. God was protecting his servant.

God was directing other events as well. The national leader who had insisted that Andre be put to death, was assassinated. The soldiers, fearing for their lives at this turn of events, left the village and went into hiding.

Andre was able to get out of the grave that he had been forced to dig for himself and continue his preaching. People were amazed. They thought they were seeing a ghost! They realized that Andre's God had protected him and were at last ready to listen to his message.

Andre is still a lay preacher in Chad, Africa, busy telling people about the true God.

STOP

400 words

The Most Important Lesson
Part 1

Note these words:
Tomiko (tō•mē•kō) Akita (ä•kē•tä) Teiko (tĕ•ē•kō)

"I have returned!" called out Tomiko as she slid open the front door of her home in Akita, Japan.

"Welcome home!" replied her mother coming out of the kitchen where she was preparing vegetables for the evening meal.

"May I go play with Teiko San?" asked Tomiko eagerly, putting her bag of schoolbooks on the floor.

Mother shook her head. "Not today, Tomiko. There is no time now to play. Tonight you will start your English lessons, remember?"

Tomiko's lip came out in a pout. "I don't need English lessons, Mother. I am learning English at school."

"Oh, but this is a rare opportunity, Tomiko," answered Mother. "This teacher is an American. You will learn correct English pronunciation from her."

Tomiko started to protest, but realized it was no use. Her mother and father were determined that she should have the best education possible. She would need it to compete in the new Japan, they always said.

When the three of them sat down on their cushions around the low table in the living room to eat their evening meal, Tomiko asked her father about the old Japan he lived in as a boy.

"We were poor," he said. "People lived in small simple houses. We could not afford to eat meat, only fish once in a while with our rice. We did not have a car, only a bicycle for transportation or the public buses and trains."

"We could never have afforded to learn English from an American," Mother put in. "Think of the privilege that is yours, to learn proper English pronunciation. Hurry and eat now. It is soon time to go."

Tomiko began to eat the rice, deep fried pork, and soup that her mother had prepared. She did not look forward to going to another class when she had been in school all day, but there was no way to get out of it.

After the meal, her father went out to start the car. Tomiko followed, still unwilling. She sighed. Maybe it would have been better to be a child in the old days when almost everyone was poor. Why were Father and Mother so determined she get a good education?

Father seemed to read her thoughts as he started the car. "It is a different world today, Tomiko," he said. "The world is changing rapidly and Japan must keep up. Our youth must get a good education in order to compete with other countries. It is a great opportunity for you to learn English from an American!"

(to be continued)

425 words

The Most Important Lesson
Part 2

Note this word:
daijobo (dä•ī•jō•bo͞o)

Tomiko's parents insist that she take English lessons so that she will get the best possible education. Tomiko doesn't want to, but knows she has no choice.

Tomiko felt shy when she entered the Christian church where the English class was to be held. She was pleasantly surprised to see her friend, Teiko, there.

"I didn't know you were coming to this class," whispered Tomiko, taking the seat next to her.

"I didn't either, but Mother says it's a great opportunity." She shrugged. "I guess so, but there are things I would rather be doing."

The American lady standing in the front was pretty. She said she was a grandmother but looked too young for that. Carefully Tomiko pronounced the English words after the teacher when it was her turn. It was hard to get the "th" in "thank you" correct. Tomiko and the other students were used to saying "sank you," and their teacher at school did not correct them.

It was quite a challenge, and the hour passed quickly. The teacher closed her book and said, "Now it is time for chapel."

Chapel? What did she mean? Tomiko soon found out. The teacher was a Christian, and after each English class she wanted her students to have a short lesson in her religion. A young woman came in and began to talk to the children about Jesus Christ Whom she said was the true God. She spoke in Japanese so that the children could understand.

Tomiko had never heard the stories of Jesus before and was fascinated. How different it was from the teaching of the Buddhist priests in the temple. She was eager to learn more, but would her parents approve? Perhaps it would be best not even to tell them.

When Tomiko's father came to pick her up, he asked her eagerly about her first lesson from the American teacher.

Tomiko shrugged and answered, "Daijobu," which means, "It was all right." She did not tell her father about the chapel time and the exciting things she had learned. He might forbid her to go back to the English class and she would never find out the rest of the story of Jesus.

Was it true that He was God as the teacher had said? Could He really forgive her sins and give her eternal life? Could she be sure she would go to a beautiful place called Heaven when she died?

It was all so strange, but Tomiko was determined to learn more. She could hardly wait until next Friday. Besides, it was the Friday before Christmas, and the teacher had promised them a party. She said she would make American cookies and candy for them. She also promised them each a Christmas gift.

What would it be? Tomiko could hardly wait to find out.

(to be continued)

470 words

The Most Important Lesson

Part 3

Tomiko went to the English class and was fascinated by the stories of Jesus she heard from the American teacher.

It would soon be Christmas. The Japanese did not celebrate this holiday in old Japan. What did the birth of Jesus so many years ago have to do with them? They had their own gods.

As time went on, however, and Japan was introduced to western influences, the Japanese adopted the Christmas holiday. For the majority of people in Japan it was not a time to thank Jesus for coming to earth to be their Savior. They knew little or nothing about this. It was merely a time to decorate the stores with lights and tinsel, buy presents, and earn extra money. Japan's real holiday was New Year's.

Tomiko was excited about going to English class the Friday before Christmas because of the party the teacher had promised them. She also hoped to hear more stories about Jesus.

Sure enough, they had their party. The cookies and candy were delicious, but what really fascinated Tomiko was the walnut the teacher showed them after they had finished their refreshments. She called it a "Gospel Nut."

The walnut did not have nutmeats inside. These had been removed and replaced by strips of colored ribbon, glued together end to end and rolled up inside the walnut. The teacher pulled out the ribbon, displaying one color at a time and explained what each color meant.

The first ribbon was black. "This stands for sin," explained the teacher. "The Bible tells us that all of us have sinned, done wrong things such as lying, being unkind to others, and so on."

Tomiko lowered her eyes. It was true. She remembered that just yesterday she had told her mother a lie.

"Sin cannot enter Heaven," went on the teacher, "but Jesus provided a way for us to get rid of our sins. He died on the cross to pay for them."

As she said these words, she pulled the ribbon and the red part appeared. "The red ribbon stands for the blood of Jesus that He shed for us on the cross. That is how He paid for our sins. When we ask Him to forgive our sins, He washes our hearts as white as snow." The teacher revealed a white ribbon.

"And that is not all," she went on, as she displayed the last ribbon which was gold in color, "those who believe in Jesus and ask Him to forgive their sins will be allowed to go to Heaven someday where the streets are paved with gold."

The teacher paused to let her words sink in, then said, "You, too, can believe in Him if you are willing."

Tomiko's heart beat fast with excitement. Yes, she believed, even if the story was too good to be true. Would she dare to share the wonderful secret with her parents? Yes, she must tell them so that they, too, could believe in Jesus and someday go to the city where the streets are paved with gold.

510 words

Village Boy of Mexico

Part 1

Note this word:
Manuel (män·wĕl′)

Manuel swung his hoe on the steep mountainside. He did not feel like working in his father's field. He would rather go to school. It had been so interesting to go and learn how to read and write.

The teacher had told the village children that if they learned to read and write, they could become rich like the Mexicans who lived in the cities.

Manuel looked down at the large, beautiful houses of the Mexicans in the valley. They had many things the village people did not have. Their houses were twice as big as Manuel's hut. Instead of grass roofs, they had tile on theirs. Their children had toys—tops and marbles. They ate delicious meals and even sucked on candy between meals.

"Manuel," cried Father harshly, as he came up behind him. "Why aren't you hoeing? Going to school has made you lazy! Get busy now. If we do not work, we will have no food to eat."

Reluctantly, Manuel turned back to his hoeing. He felt sad. Father did not understand how much he wanted to keep going to school to learn about the outside world, the world beyond their mountains.

With a sigh, Manuel tackled the weeds around the cornstalks with his hoe. His mother needed the corn in order to make tortillas. His mouth watered as he thought of food. It seemed he never had enough to satisfy him. If only he were rich like the Mexicans in the valley.

Suddenly, movement on the trail below caught Manuel's attention. Visitors did not come to their village often. Who could these people be? Manuel leaned on his hoe and stared.

Manuel sucked in his breath in surprise. He could see the travelers better now. One of them was a white man! He was very tall and pale as death. Manuel's heart beat fast with excitement. Why was a white man from the United States coming to their little village?

Manuel soon found out that the American man had come to teach the village people about his God. He had brought his young wife along to help him.

Manuel, together with the other village boys, peeked through the windows of the small house the missionaries had moved into. How strange these foreigners were! The wife stood while she cooked for her husband, then sat down to eat with him. Before they ate, they always closed their eyes.

Manuel found out many other interesting things about the American man who had come to his village. He did not get drunk or beat his wife like the village men did. He was kind to everyone. He had come to teach the people about his God, but first he must learn their language. He asked Manuel to help him.

How excited Manuel was for this opportunity! As he helped the American teacher learn the language of his people, Manuel was learning something too. He was learning about the teacher's God.

(to be continued)

485 words

Village Boy of Mexico

Part 2

Manuel longs to be rich like the Mexicans that live in the cities.

A missionary has come to his village, and Manuel is helping the American learn the language of his people.

Manuel was amazed to discover that the teacher believed in a God he could not see. Manuel could *see* his gods, all six of them sitting solemnly on the low shelf in his home. Every day Mother gathered the family to pray to them.

Manuel felt troubled. Which were the true gods,

his family's or his teacher's? He had to find out.

One day while his mother was busy pounding corn for tortillas, Manuel searched in her sewing basket until he found a long needle. Looking nervously behind him to make sure nobody was watching, he moved toward the gods with the long needle.

Manuel's mouth felt dry and his heart pounded furiously when he realized what he was about to do—stick the needle into the foot of one of the gods. If the foot bled, Manuel would know the god was alive and would believe on him as well as the other five gods. If the foot did not bleed, Manuel would know the god was only a wooden idol and would believe on the teacher's God.

Taking a deep breath, Manuel thrust the needle into the foot of the first god on the dusty shelf. The needle broke. The foot did not bleed.

Manuel ran and told his mother what he had done. "They are not real gods, Mother," he cried. "The teacher's God is the true God. I will follow Him."

Manuel's mother became very upset. "You have insulted the gods!" she cried, wringing her hands in despair. "You will die in thirty minutes!"

Manuel did not die, but something else happened. Because he determined to believe in and follow the teacher's God, his father became very angry and chased him out of his house.

The missionary took Manuel into his home. For a whole year, Manuel helped the missionary learn the language of his people. Then he got a job working for a missionary in Mexico

City where he could attend school at the same time.

Manuel went to many schools after that, not only in Mexico City, but also in Canada, the United States, and Germany. He learned six languages besides his own.

Manuel's boyhood dream was to live in a big house, to own a top and marbles, and to have candy and other delicious treats to eat. Now that he had an education, he could have all that and much more, but Manuel had discovered a different kind of riches—he had come to know the true God and His Son, Jesus Christ. He determined to spend the rest of his life sharing these eternal riches with his people.

Manuel returned to his people and started a school for them. At his school Manuel trains young men to do many useful things, but especially he trains them to teach people about the true God and His Word. Manuel is happy as he shares his eternal riches with his people.

STOP

515 words

A Testing Time

Part 1

Note these words:
Hwangyuan (hwäng·ywĕn)
overlord: *one in a position of power*

Why do Christians sometimes have to suffer? Can God not deliver them quickly as He did Daniel from the lions' den? Oh, yes, He can, but sometimes God lets us go through hard times to show unbelievers His great power. Then, too, the way believers endure suffering is an encouragement to other Christians.

Arthur and Wilda Mathews were missionaries in north China when the Communists controlled the country. Many missionaries were unable to continue their work under the new government, but amazingly, the Mathews were invited to stay in China to work with the Mongols in the far north. The Chinese church had invited them, and the Communist government had given their consent. Together with their 13-month-old baby, Lilah, the couple made their way to the town of Hwangyuan, on the edge of the great Tibetan grasslands.

When they arrived at their destination, they were

met by two Chinese pastors, but not warmly welcomed as they expected. Under the Communist government, it was dangerous to be too friendly with the hated "imperialists" as the Australians and Americans were called (Arthur was an Australian and Wilda an American). Only their darling baby seemed to be welcome.

The missionaries were shown to their living quarters, a small kitchen with a workbench and a huge iron stove, and a bedroom located at a distance away from the kitchen. It was unheated and icy cold in the wintertime. The rest of the house had been given over to a Chinese doctor to use as a hospital.

The missionaries did their best to settle into their simple quarters and began their study of the Mongolian language. The first Sunday they were there, Arthur was asked to preach at the morning service. He did this joyfully and also volunteered to go with some of the Christians to preach in the surrounding villages.

The Christians soon discouraged him from doing this, however. It was obvious that they were afraid of displeasing their Communist overlords. The foreign missionaries were making their position even more dangerous.

One of Arthur's first tasks was to rent a house which he fixed up as a clinic to serve the people. It was also a place from which to distribute literature. When he was all ready to move in, he was told that a Chinese troop had taken it over for another purpose. To make matters worse, a policeman came and informed the missionaries that they were not allowed to perform any public ministries and must stay in their small rooms.

There they were in their little kitchen with only a table, two chairs, and a child's rocking chair. They put a trunk in the corner, and that is where they knelt to pray. There they brought their confusion and disappointment to the Lord and received His comfort.

When Arthur and Wilda realized that they would not be permitted to go out and minister to the people, they applied for exit permits to leave China. They had found out that all missionaries of their mission society were to leave China, as their presence only put the Chinese Christians in danger.

(to be continued)

510 words

A Testing Time
Part 2

The Mathews are missionaries to China. They have decided they must leave because their presence is endangering the Chinese Christians.

Because the Mathews had applied for exit visas and expected to leave China any time, they got rid of most of their possessions. They took down their curtains, gathered together their linens and dishes, and sold them. All they kept were a few tin plates, bowls, and mugs that would be useful on their truck journey to the coast where they would leave for their homeland.

Besides these items, blankets and their clothing would be all they would need for their trip. They had no idea that it would be more than two years before they would be permitted to leave.

If they had been allowed to preach in the church and teach the Bible to the people around them, they would not have minded staying, even with bare walls and cupboards, but this was not permitted. Gradually even the few Chinese Christians who had shown them friendliness at first stopped coming to see them. These people were afraid of getting into trouble with the government if they associated with the despised "imperialists" as the foreigners were called.

The Christians in the homeland who were supporting the missionaries were sending in their money faithfully, but the Mathews could not receive it directly. It had to go to a Chinese bank first and be changed into Chinese currency.

Although the money came to the bank every month, the Mathews family was never notified of it. Arthur had to go each month and beg for the money that had come for him and his family. He had to be very careful in his request so as not to offend the officials or the money would be denied him. It was humiliating for him to go each month, sometimes many times, before his request would be granted.

Meanwhile the missionaries had to try to stretch their meager supplies. Often they ran out of things before the money was finally given to them.

They had to buy coal for their stove (northern China

is very cold in the winter), milk for little Lilah, and food to last them until their next month's money would arrive. The officials made Arthur feel like a beggar even though he was requesting what was rightfully his. They were actually trying to get rid of the foreigners by starving them to death.

Arthur joined the poor people of the town who went out to the hillsides to gather dried leaves and grass roots, collecting anything that would burn. Arthur even brought home sheep manure which he mixed with coal dust and made into balls for fuel.

Often when the officials delayed in producing the needed money, God supplied for them from other sources. At one time when they were completely out of salt, a Russian Christian who sold salt gave them a good supply. One memorable evening the Russian's young daughter brought them a basket containing about ten pounds of meat before scurrying away so she would not be seen by the authorities. Someone else gave them some sugar and raisins. What a treat that was!

During this difficult time, the missionaries learned to trust God and thank Him for everything, even the difficulties they were experiencing.

(to be continued)

550 words

A Testing Time

Part 3

The Mathews are learning to trust God for their daily needs as they wait more than two years to be permitted to leave China.

The Mathews wanted to give their little girl, Lilah, a birthday party when she turned three years old. They had no money with which to buy toys or the ingredients for a birthday cake, but Mrs. Mathews was very clever at sewing. She found some old material and made a doll from it for her little daughter.

Lilah already had a worn out teddy bear and bunny, and a duck made of oilcloth. Together with her new doll, these were the only "friends" she could have at her party since the Chinese children she used to play with were not allowed to come to their house anymore.

How happy Lilah became on her birthday when there was a knock at the door and there stood two Russian children who had come to play with her. They had been afraid to come before and never came again, but how good of the Lord to send them on her birthday to make the day so special.

Meanwhile, the Communist government was making repeated promises to the missionaries that they would be allowed to leave on such and such a day, but they always went back on their promises. The missionaries learned to trust God to do what was best for them. They certainly could not trust men. How their patience must have encouraged the Chinese Christians who were also going through trials under the Communist government.

The seventh time the authorities promised to release the missionaries, permission came for Mrs. Mathews and Lilah to leave, but not Arthur. When Mrs. Mathews asked the policeman why her husband could not leave, he said, "Your husband is a criminal."

It was difficult for Arthur to say good-bye to his little family, but he had confidence that God would take care of them and eventually provide release for him, too.

Arthur was at this time receiving letters from the homeland, telling of how many had been encouraged by the way the Mathews had trusted God and endured their suffering. These letters gave him much joy. He knew that what they had gone through was all for a purpose. He also knew that in God's time, he, too, would be delivered, no matter what the Communists planned against him. God's promises became very precious to him at this time.

One day as he was watering a few vegetables in his garden, he saw a policeman approaching him. To his great surprise, the officer told him to get ready to leave in an hour. Later, as he sat in the police vehicle and realized he was on his way to freedom, he said to himself, "This is the Lord's doing, and it is marvelous!"

Arthur had to go through other questioning and accusations on his trip to Hong Kong. He was even locked up in a jail for a short time, but at last he was released. He was on his way to freedom and reunion with his family! This was in 1953, after more than two years of suspense.

This story shows that God will help us in our troubles, too, and make everything work together for our good.

STOP

550 words

Anatole's Adventure

Note these words:
Anatole (än·ä·tō·lē) sergeant (sär′jənt)

Anatole was a brilliant young man, but his teachers did not honor him. They never gave him more than a C grade for his good work. The reason for this was that Anatole was a Christian during the time when Communists were in control of the Soviet Union.

Anatole and his family lived in the part of the former Soviet Union called the Ukraine. They were the only Christians in their town.

Finally Anatole became discouraged. He decided there was only one way to get along in a Communist country. He would renounce his faith and accept Communism. Anatole walked away from God and joined the Communist party.

The Communists were delighted to see a Christian turn away from God and join their ranks. They were excited to have this brilliant young man on their side. Quickly they promoted him to be a sergeant in the Soviet Army.

No longer was Anatole harassed and ridiculed. No longer were his talents and abilities ignored. He was admired and respected.

Was Anatole happy in his new role as a Communist? No, he was miserable. How could he deny his Savior Who had died for him and join his enemies? Anatole could not continue to do so. He humbly returned to God, asking Him for forgiveness.

Anatole gave up his brilliant career, choosing rather to become a pastor.

By this time, the Soviet Union had changed from being a strict Communist state into the Commonwealth of Independent States (C.I.S.). Although Christians were often ridiculed by many who were still Communists, they were permitted to teach and preach about the true God without being punished.

Anatole returned to his village of 7,000 people and started a church in his parents' home. Soon there were sixty people attending.

Anatole also preached about Christ in the surrounding villages. There too, people turned to the Lord.

A young American Christian named Scott heard about Pastor Anatole and felt led by God to help him in his ministry. He sent money to support the young pastor whenever he could. He also prayed much for him. Finally Scott was able to take a trip to the Ukraine to meet Anatole in person. He was not a wealthy young man, but he had been able to save $500 to take with him to help Anatole in his work for the Lord.

Meanwhile Anatole had been trying to save money for a used car in which to go to the villages to preach. He could not get through the heavy snow in the winter on his bicycle. At last he had been able to save $200, but it was not enough.

How happy Anatole was when Scott visited him in his village and he found out that Scott was interested in helping him by praying and supporting his ministry. When Scott presented him with the $500 he had brought, Anatole was overjoyed. With the $200 he had saved, there would be enough for a used car. Now he could continue to preach in the villages during the winter months. God had wonderfully answered his prayer!

What a privilege it is to help people learn about the Savior Who can forgive their sins and give them eternal life. What a privilege it is to share what we have with those who have so little.

535 words

Yochi's Front Teeth

Part 1

Note these words:
Yochi (yō·chē) Sauko (sou·kō)

Yochi watched spellbound as his friend's front teeth were sawed off by two of the village men. The boy suddenly realized he was shaking. He moved a little farther away from the horrible sight, but he could not keep his eyes off Sauko.

It was not sympathy for his friend that made Yochi tremble. He was thinking of when he, too, must go through the horrible ordeal. All of the tribes boys of the mountains of Vietnam had to have their front teeth sawed off when they had lived thirteen summers.

Yochi sighed deeply. He had already lived ten summers. Before long it would be his turn. The boy shuddered at the thought; he was glad when the ceremony was over.

Yochi found his grandmother busy husking rice. Pound, pound, pound sounded the heavy stick on the flat rock. The breeze blew away the husks, leaving the rice ready for cooking.

Yochi usually kept away from Grandmother when she was working. She might ask him to help, and he would much rather play. But today he was too troubled to join in the mischief of the other boys.

"Doubly old Mother," he began respectfully, "tell me, why do the mountain boys have to have their front teeth sawed off?" Grandmother stopped pounding and sat back on her heels, pushing a long strand of black hair from her eyes.

"You know, Yochi," she answered. "Men who don't have their front teeth sawed off look like animals and act wild and fierce like animals, too. No girl will marry them."

Yochi made a little hole in the dirt with his big toe as he pondered his grandmother's words. Finally he looked up.

"But what if I don't want to get married?"

Grandmother looked shocked. "Of course you want to get married, Yochi. Someday your mother and I will die. Then who will cook rice for you if you don't have a wife?"

Yochi had no answer to that question. True, he did not want to grow up mean like a wild animal, and he would need a wife like everyone else. Gingerly he felt his front teeth, imagining how it would feel to have the rough saw go through them.

Grandmother understood. "Little one, don't be afraid. When you have lived for thirteen summers you will be so big you won't mind." The old woman turned back to her work, and Yochi, still not comforted, walked slowly toward the river.

Across the river swung the vine bridge the men of the village had built. Yochi started to run lightly across when suddenly he stopped. Someone was coming down the trail toward the bridge! Frightened, Yochi ran back into the protection of the forest. It might be Communist soldiers from the north. Swiftly he climbed a banyan tree and hid behind its thick foliage.

Then he saw them, not Communist soldiers as he had feared, but strange-looking creatures with white skin! There were as many as the fingers on one of Yochi's brown hands!

Yochi almost laughed in spite of his fear as he watched them cross the swaying vine bridge. They were so clumsy! What kind of creatures were they, anyway?

(to be continued)

530 words

Yochi's Front Teeth
Part 2

Yochi dreads the time when his front teeth will be sawed off as is the custom among the mountain boys of Vietnam when they have lived thirteen summers.

Yochi, the mountain boy of Vietnam, was surprised when from his perch in a banyan tree, he watched a strange group of white people coming down the trail that led to his village. The mountain boy was afraid to stay in the banyan tree with the strange creatures approaching. He worried that they might cast a spell on him. Swiftly he dropped down from his hiding place and ran to the village.

When Yochi arrived at the village he was so out of breath he could hardly speak. His round, terrified eyes spoke for him. Everyone gathered around the frightened boy.

"They're coming—up—up the trail," he managed at last, "strange, queer ones—" He did not need to say more, for at that instant the men entered Stony Ridge Village.

Yochi watched in amazement as the village elders invited the strangers to sit with them around the campfire. He had not noticed until then that one of the strangers had brown skin like the tribes people. He could speak the language of the mountains.

One of the white men who seemed to be the leader, made strange sounds.

Everyone laughed at him. The brown-skinned man put the strange sounds into mountain language.

Yochi listened spellbound, but he did not hear much of what the strange men were saying. He was too busy staring at their teeth. They were not sawed off like the tribesmen's.

"They have teeth like an animal," mused the boy, "so they must be fierce and wild people." Yochi edged a little closer to Grandmother, who was gaping at the strangers with her mouth open.

The white people, who turned out to be missionaries, came back often to Stony Ridge Village. They brought medicine for the sick people and taught the people about the true God who loved them and sent His Son to die for them. They taught that all men were sinners. Sawing off the teeth did not change them to good, kind people, but the true God could change them if they asked Him. He had sent His Son to the world to die in order to make men good.

One day in his favorite banyan tree near the river, Yochi asked God to take away his badness and make him good. He promised God that he would not worship the evil spirits anymore, but would follow Him and His Son, Jesus, always.

Yochi felt happy as he scrambled out of the banyan tree and started back to the village. Even the future tooth-sawing did not seem so terrible now.

One night around their campfire Yochi's father and mother talked about what they learned from the missionaries.

"I have decided to follow the God of the skies," announced Father.

"I, too, Father," said Yochi quietly, prodding the embers of the fire with a stick.

Mother and Grandmother looked anxiously behind them, afraid the evil spirits had heard the bold words and would be angry.

Rice planting time came and the harvest was gathered in. Yochi's mother and grandmother, together with many other villagers, believed in the God of the skies that the missionaries told them about and became His followers.

Eventually Yochi had lived for thirteen summers. It was time for the teeth-sawing ceremony.

"You will not have your teeth sawed," declared Yochi's father firmly. "Jesus is the One Who tames our wildness and takes away our badness."

"But what about a wife?" questioned Grandmother.

"He will have a Christian wife," declared Father, "one who believes as we do."

Yochi grinned as he rubbed his thumb back and forth over his front teeth. He was glad for more than one reason that the missionaries had brought their message of the God of the skies to Stony Ridge Village.

660 words

Detour to Joy

Note these words:
Pasha (pä′shə) Shura (shūr′ə)
happy-go-lucky: *easy-going; lighthearted*

Pasha was excited. He and his sister, Shura, were going with their parents from their home in Russia to Siberia. There they would be able to buy land cheap. What an adventure!

Things did not turn out as they had expected. Both of Pasha's parents became ill on the way because of poor food and impure water and were taken to a hospital for treatment.

Pasha and Shura waited anxiously for word of their parents' recovery only to learn that their parents had both died.

The children were taken to an orphanage. Pasha hated it from the beginning. The food tasted terrible. He was separated from his sister. He determined to run away the first chance he had.

One dark night he climbed over the wall and ran as far away from the orphanage as possible. When he could run no more, he lay down on the hard ground to sleep.

In the morning a robber gang discovered the sleeping boy and slapped him awake. When Pasha told them of his parents' death and his escape from the orphanage, the robber gang decided to take him along with them.

Pasha joined the gang and became a robber. He learned to steal and even to kill. By the time he was sixteen years old, he had become one of the leaders of the gang.

One day as he and a companion robbed and killed two men, they found a Bible among their victim's possessions. Pasha was about to throw it away when his companion said, "Let's keep it. We can use the paper to roll cigarettes."

That evening as Pasha opened the Bible, his mind was flooded with memories of his childhood. This was the Book his mother used to read.

Instead of tearing out the pages to roll cigarettes, Pasha began to read them. He read far into the night. He was especially impressed with Jesus' forgiveness of the thief on the cross. Would Jesus forgive him as well for all the wicked things he had done?

The next day the happy-go-lucky leader of the robber gang was strangely quiet and thoughtful. When his companions asked what had come over him, he told them it was the Book he had found on the travelers the day before.

"Read it to us," said the men.

Pasha read the Bible to the robber gang every day for a month. As a result, Pasha and six of his companions decided to leave the gang and follow Christ.

After making this decision, they went to the nearest police station and turned themselves in. The authorities sent them to a prison camp in Siberia.

While in prison, the converted robbers shared their new-found faith with the other prisoners. Many of them decided to follow Christ. One day the authorities released Pasha for good behavior. Then he was free to travel from village to village to tell people about the Book that had changed his life.

At one cottage, he met a woman who was also a Christian. As he told her what God had done for him, she became excited.

"You are Pasha, my long-lost brother!" she cried.

How happy they were to find each other!

"Let us go back to our home village and tell the people there the wonderful message of the Bible that has changed our lives!" declared Pasha, and that is exactly what they did.

570 words

The Domino Effect

Note these words:
Sumiko (sōō·mē·kō) tuberculosis (tōō·bûr′kyə·lō′sĭs)
Onuma (ō·nōō·mä) Saito (sä·ē·tō)
prejudice: *an opinion that someone has before he knows all the facts*

Have you ever played dominoes? After playing the game, no doubt you have stood the dominoes on end and made a long, winding row of them. When all are ready, you touch the first domino. It falls on the next one and so on until all the dominoes are down. It's fun to watch the domino effect.

This story is about a different kind of domino effect. It tells how our witnessing for Jesus can affect not only one person, but many in the end.

A missionary had told a Japanese girl, Sumiko, in Sakata, Japan, about Jesus and she had believed in Him. Sumiko was glad to be a Christian but discouraged about other things. Her sister had died from tuberculosis and now Sumiko, too, had the disease. Her parents finally agreed to put her in a hospital for tuberculosis patients.

Sumiko soon overcame her discouragement as she realized that God had sent her to the hospital to be a light for her Savior. The sick people with whom she lived each day were usually willing to listen to her testimony about Jesus.

One young woman, named Onuma, was especially eager to hear about Sumiko's Savior. She realized the gods of her childhood could not help her, and eventually opened her heart to Jesus. Do you see the domino effect? The missionary led Sumiko to the Lord, then Sumiko helped Onuma find Him.

That, however, is not the end of the story. There was a young man in the hospital named Mr. Saito who was attracted to the sweet, gentle Onuma. Mr. Saito had been an army officer in World War II and hated the Americans who had conquered his country. He wanted nothing to do with their religion. He was, however, beginning to love Onuma, even though she had embraced the foreigners' Christianity.

Much to Mr. Saito's dismay, Onuma's physical condition gradually worsened. One day, still rejoicing in her Savior, she passed away. Mr. Saito was devastated. When Sumiko and the missionaries held a Christian memorial service for her at the hospital, he came, in spite of his dislike for Americans and their religion.

Mr. Saito was impressed with the joyful look on Sumiko's face as she sang with the missionaries, "There is a land that is fairer than day." The missionary spoke of that land where all is joy, peace, and light. He said that Onuma had gone there and would be happy there forever and ever.

In spite of his prejudices against Americans and Christianity, Mr. Saito began to consider becoming a Christian as his girlfriend had. He began to read the New Testament the missionary gave him. After some time, he gave up his prejudice and became a follower of Christ.

Mr. Saito was respected at the hospital, not only by the other patients, but by the staff as well. As he grew as a Christian, he became a powerful witness for God, influencing others in the hospital to come to Christ.

Eventually both Sumiko and Mr. Saito died from their disease. Both of them went to be with the Lord and with Onuma who had gone before them. Their testimony at the hospital lived on, however, and the other patients turned to Christ.

Do you see the domino effect? The missionary led Sumiko to the Lord. She won Onuma. Onuma influenced Mr. Saito to become a Christian. Mr. Saito influenced a number of other patients to come to Christ. Who knows the end of it all?

When we witness for the Lord we have no idea how many people will ultimately be affected by our testimony. Not until we get to Heaven will we discover how our witness has reached not one person only, but others as well. Isn't it exciting to be part of this domino effect?

605 words

Rescued Two Ways

Note these words:
Kaboo (kä·bo͞o) Kru (kro͞o)

The African youth, Kaboo, watched, horrified, as his captors dug a pit for him. He knew that they intended to bury him up to his neck, smear his mouth with a sweet substance, then watch as driver ants ate him alive.

If only his father could ransom him! The Kru tribe, of which his father was chief, had been beaten in war. His father was forced to give him to the victors as a hostage. He could not meet the huge demands for his son's ransom.

Kaboo had been beaten with thorny poison vines until he was very weak and ill, but as he watched his tormentors dig a pit for him, from somewhere he got the idea to make a dash for his freedom. Later he realized it was God who put the daring idea into his mind and gave him the strength to attempt it.

He did not understand how he managed to escape into the forest without his captors seeing him. He did not know how he was able to hide from them when they found him missing and came in hot pursuit. He did not understand how he survived in the jungle full of enemy tribes, wild beasts, and poisonous snakes. All he knew was that Someone, Whom he did not know or understand, was protecting and leading him.

How else could he explain that after days of stumbling through the forests, crossing rivers, and living on wild fruit and grasses, he finally came to a friendly foreign settlement? It could have been a colony of slave-traders; instead, it was a settlement of slave-liberators (people who set slaves free) near Monrovia, the capital of Liberia.

Kaboo found a job at the settlement and started to work. One day he met a boy from the Kru tribe to which he belonged. This friend had become a Christian and invited Kaboo to go with him to hear the missionaries.

As Kaboo heard the story of Jesus Christ, he believed almost immediately. He knew that some great power had enabled him to escape being eaten alive. Someone greater than he had led him through the trackless forest to this place of safety.

Eagerly Kaboo began to study his Bible. When he was baptized, he changed his name from Kaboo to Sammy Morris.

After learning all he could from the missionary, he decided to go to America for further study. He had no money, but set out for the coast on foot to find a ship for America. The captain of a ship finally took him on as a cabin boy.

When he arrived in the United States and began going to school, the African boy was surprised to see that many Christians did not seem to be excited about knowing God. They had become citizens of Heaven, even as he had, yet they were more interested in things of earth. Sammy prayed much for them, and also for fellow students who had no time for God. How happy he was when God worked in the lives of these students.

Sammy could not get over the wonder of his salvation. Jesus Christ had not only rescued him from a horrible physical death, but from eternal death as well. He could not thank and praise God enough for the eternal life He had given him.

Sammy Morris wanted to go back to his people and tell them about the One who had saved him, but God had other plans. When he was just 21 years of age and still in school, God took the African youth to Himself. Through his death, many fellow students dedicated their lives to God and went to the ends of the earth with the wonderful message of His love.

STOP

630 words

The Bread, Cake, and Candy Man

Note these words:
Tachiro Morinaga (tä·chē·rō mōr·ē·nä·gä)
embassy: *the office of a government representative in a foreign country*

Tachiro Morinaga was alone and penniless in a strange country. He had come from Japan to the United States to sell his uncle's pottery, but the business had failed.

Tachiro had known little but hardship during his life. His father died when he was a young boy leaving him to the mercy of not-so-kind relatives. He had to start earning his living when he was twelve, working for a writing master, a grocer, and then for his uncle who was a pottery merchant. Now in his twenties he was "broke" and stranded in a foreign country.

Tachiro decided to get work as a servant in a well-to-do home. It must have been God who led him to a kind Christian lady who hired him at once. Tachiro began to waver when he saw how kind and unselfish his new Christian friends were. Finally he began to read the Bible for himself.

Gradually, as he read the Bible, Tachiro began to understand the love of God and His plan for man through His Son, Jesus Christ. When he was 26 years old, he believed in Jesus as his personal Savior and was baptized. That was in 1900.

After he became a Christian, Tachiro worked for six years to pay off the debt which came with his business failure. Then he decided to return to Japan; but what should his business be?

In those days the Japanese did not eat bread, only rice three times a day to go with their fish, meat, and vegetables. They did not have cake as we do, only little delicacies made from sweet bean paste. They did not have cookies like we have, only salty crackers often with a seaweed flavor. Chocolate was almost unknown.

Tachiro Morinaga decided that he would introduce western-style bread, cake, cookies, and candy to Japan. In order to do this he had to learn how to produce these items. He secured work first in a bakery and then in a candy factory. After learning the secrets of making good bread, cake, and candy, he returned to his homeland.

Settling in Tokyo, Tachiro began his business. At first he had trouble selling his products. They were so new and different, nobody wanted to try them. He was not, however, interested only in selling his bread and cakes; he also wanted to tell people about Jesus Christ Who had become his Savior. To do this Tachiro put large gold letters above his delivery car with these words, "Christ Jesus Came Into the World to Save Sinners."

Two things happened: people began to buy bread and cakes, and they began to listen to Tachiro's message about Jesus.

One day a man from the American embassy discovered in Tokyo, a Japanese man who was making American-style bread and cakes. Delighted, he told his American friends, who all began to buy from Tachiro.

Then the Imperial Household of the emperor began to get interested in Tachiro's western-style bakery items. Business began to boom. After a few years, Tachiro Morinaga had many people working for him, and his products became known throughout all Japan as well as Korea. People called him "The Chocolate King" because of the delicious chocolate candy he introduced to Japan.

Wherever his business took him, Tachiro Morinaga told people about Jesus Christ and what He could do for them. Nobody knows how many people became Christians through his influence.

Today there are other varieties of western-style cake, cookies, and chocolate in Japan, but Morinaga products are still popular and widely sold.

When Tachiro Morinaga passed away he left not only bread, cake, and chocolate candy for the Japanese people, but also the strong testimony of a Christian businessman who was not afraid to stand up for Jesus Christ wherever he went.

665 words

A Bulldog, a Goat, and an Elephant

Note these words:
Shan (shän) Sawbwa (säw·bwä)

God usually does His work through people, but one time, at least, He used three animals: a bulldog, a goat, and an elephant.

A missionary doctor had gone to Burma to minister to the Shan people. He opened his well-equipped office and waited for people to come for medical help. Nobody came.

The reason they did not come was that their ruler, called the Sawbwa, did not approve of the American missionary. The people were afraid they would get into trouble with their ruler if they went to see the doctor.

What could the doctor do? He just had to pray and wait for God to work. The answer to his prayers came quite unexpectedly. One day a man came to the dispensary leading a bulldog. He handed the doctor a letter decorated with the royal seals. It was from the great Sawbwa. The ruler was asking the missionary to please treat his dog who had a bad toothache.

The missionary doctor had never in his practice treated animals before, but decided to do his best to relieve the dog's pain. He gave him a shot, then pulled the offending tooth. That took care of the bulldog's discomfort, and he happily followed the man back to his master.

Two weeks later, the missionary saw the Sawbwa's servant coming up the path again. This time he was leading a goat. The servant handed the doctor a letter from the Sawbwa stating that his goat, which he had obtained in Switzerland, was suffering from an earache. Would the doctor please cure him as he had cured his bulldog?

This was more of a challenge for the doctor than the bulldog was, but he determined to do what he could. Examining the animal's ears in his dispensary, he found a large amount of wax which he removed. Bowing his thanks, the servant led the goat away.

One day later when the missionary and his wife were eating breakfast, they discovered the Sawbwa's servant had come again, this time riding a huge elephant. The missionary trembled. What was expected of him now?

The elephant's keeper shouted an order to the elephant who immediately dropped to his knees. The keeper then showed the doctor a large boil beneath the elephant's ear. It needed to be cut open for the poison to escape. The missionary knew this would be painful. Would the animal allow him to do this?

The keeper assured the doctor that the elephant was always obedient. He would make him lie down on his side so the doctor could reach the boil.

The doctor used a sterilized mop and mixed up a cleaning solution in a washtub. Praying to God for help, he began to cleanse the infected place with the mop. This made the elephant angry and he tried to get up but listened to his keeper's order to lie still. Then the missionary, still praying, cut the boil with the knife which made the elephant even more angry. Again, he obeyed his master's commands and relaxed.

Soon the boil was drained and the elephant was relieved of his pain. The doctor heaved a sigh of relief as the elephant lumbered off.

One day the royal Sawbwa himself came, riding up on his elephant, followed by his attendants, to thank the missionary for treating his animals. He welcomed the missionary doctor to his country.

When the people heard that their ruler was friendly to the missionary, they were no longer afraid to come to him with their sicknesses. He was able not only to treat their physical ailments, but more important, to tell them about Jesus, Who could forgive their sins and give them eternal life.

God used a bulldog, a goat, and an elephant to reach many people with the message of Jesus. If He can use sick animals, how much more can He use boys and girls to reach others for Him? Are you willing to be used by Him to spread the good news of Jesus?

670 words

Street Boy

Samuel knew it would happen sooner or later—his father would be put in prison. The Filipino boy was only ten years old, but he had already known much sadness in his life.

Samuel was both glad and sad that the police had come to take his father away. At least there would be no more cruel beatings from him when he was drunk.

His mother was a drug addict, but she did not beat her son. Neither did she take care of him. There was nothing for Sammy to do but go out on the streets of Manila where he lived and become a beggar.

Samuel found out that life on the streets was not pleasant. Sometimes it was dangerous when boys bigger and stronger than he demanded the food he had begged or found in garbage cans.

Samuel learned to eat the food quickly before it could be taken from him by the bigger boys. He also learned to steal from boys younger than himself and hide from the police.

One day Samuel saw a group of street children listening to a kind-looking man. The man was showing the children a book. It had no words or pictures, only colored pages. Sammy pressed closer to hear what the man was saying.

"This black page stands for sin," said the man. "Everyone has sinned, done wrong things. Our hearts are as dark as this page."

Samuel did not like to look at the dark page. He did not want to think about his lies and stealing.

The man then turned to the next page in the book. It was bright red. "This page stands for the blood of Jesus," he explained. "God loves you so much He sent His Son, Jesus, to earth. Jesus took the punishment for your sins when He died on the cross. If you believe in Him and ask Him to forgive your sins, He will make your heart white and clean." The man turned to the white page.

Samuel felt a longing within him. Could he, a bad

street boy, really have a clean heart like that?

Now the man was showing the last page of the book, and it was gold colored. "The God, Who loves you and sent His Son to die for you, has prepared a beautiful place in Heaven for all those who receive His Son as their Savior," he said. "If you ask Him, He will forgive your sins and someday take you there."

Samuel did not run off as most of the other children did when the man had finished his story. He wanted to hear more. How surprised he was when the man came over to talk to him.

"Do you live on the streets?" he asked Samuel.

Sammy nodded.

"Would you like to have a clean bed to sleep in and some food to eat?"

Sammy nodded again.

"Then come with me," said the man, leading him to a jeep on the street.

It was exciting to have a ride in a jeep, but it was even more wonderful to be taken to the man's house where a kind woman was caring for other Filipino boys. They were all clean and well behaved.

The man gave Samuel some clean clothes and filled a tub with warm water for a bath. The Filipino boy was delighted. It almost seemed as if he had already reached the golden city the man talked about.

Other surprises awaited Samuel in his new home—a satisfying meal with the other boys, a cot to sleep on at night, and a promise of school the next day. He would learn to read and write. Someday he would be able to get a job and support himself. Best of all, he would be able to hear more about the God who loved him. Sammy had never been so happy.

There are hundreds of street children like Samuel in the large cities of our world waiting for someone to rescue them, waiting for someone to give them food, clothing, and especially to tell them about a God Who loves them and has a wonderful plan for their life.

695 words

When Darkness Falls
Part 1

Note these words:
Campa (căm′pə) Vishnu (vĭsh′nōō)
entranced (ĕn·trănst′): *filled with wonder*

Shouts awakened Mark from his sleep. He sat up quickly in his hammock, pushing the mosquito netting aside. Still half asleep, he jumped down from his hammock, stumbled across the floor to the door, and looked out. Then he remembered what the shouting was all about. The Campa people were welcoming their god back after the night. Their god was the sun.

Mark listened entranced to the joyous shouts. How

these people loved the sun! How they hated darkness! They believed the spirits of the dead roamed the forests at night. No wonder they slept as closely as possible to their campfires. They had nobody to protect them from the fearful darkness, because their god was gone until morning.

Thoughtfully Mark turned back into the bamboo-palm house where he lived. What would it be like to have a part-time god like the Campa people of Peru did, one that left you every night to face the darkness alone?

"Jesus, I'm glad You're with me all the time," he whispered, "not just when the sun is shining. Please help the Campa people to believe in You so they will have a God with them always as we do."

Quickly Mark pulled on his clothes. Mother, Dad, and Debbie, his younger sister, were not stirring yet. He would have time to play with his friend, Vishnu, before breakfast and morning classes.

Mark stepped out of the house and ran to the river just in time to see a group of Campa men jump into the water. They had thrown a chopped-up root to a school of fish they had sighted. The root stunned the fish and made them float about as if dead.

Mark watched, fascinated, as the men grabbed the floating fish, held them between their teeth, swam to shore, and flung them to their women to put in baskets and later roast over the fire.

Mark wished he could swim in the river with the Indians, but his father had forbidden him to do so. "The river is dangerous, son," he often said. "It is full of savage fish. Remember the man who was killed by an electric eel recently? What about the alligators who could drown you with one swish of their tail? And sometimes poisonous snakes lie in the branches that hang over the river waiting to catch a dinner. Boa constrictors swallow deer whole—they might decide to do the same to a boy."

Mark sighed as he turned away. Even though he had lived on the edge of the river for a year, he had not learned its secrets as the Campas knew them. He could venture out in it only when his father with his gun was with him.

Vishnu came walking slowly to the river's edge. He usually looked happy in the morning, but not today.

"My monkey died last night," he reported sadly.

"Bobo?"

Vishnu nodded.

Mark felt sad. The boys had spent many hours playing with Vishnu's mischievous pet.

"Maybe you can find another monkey," suggested Mark.

Vishnu shook his head while he dug his big toe into the soft sand by the river's edge.

Mark felt sorry for Vishnu. He remembered how sad he had felt when his dog was run over by a car in America. "Let's go see if we can find another one today after lessons," he said.

Mother appeared at the door of the bamboo-palm house. Mark knew it was time for breakfast.

"Right after lessons we'll go," he said as he turned to run home. "Don't forget, Vishnu."

Mark had some chores to

do after lessons and their noon meal, so it was mid-afternoon when he met his friend at the edge of the clearing and started down the jungle trail.

Bright flowers peeked through the dense foliage. Brilliantly colored birds flew from bush to tree, chirping and shrilling. Monkeys scampered about. The boys ran after them. It was such fun Mark didn't realize they had left the edge of the forest far behind.

Suddenly he felt uneasy. He was not allowed to go far into the jungle without his father and his gun.

(to be continued)

690 words

When Darkness Falls

Part 2

Note these words:
bewildered: *confused*
superstition: *a belief based on fear and ignorance rather than the Bible*

Mark, son of a missionary to Peru, had ventured into the jungle with his friend Vishnu to look for a monkey pet. He became uneasy when he realized how far they had gone into the dangerous jungle.

"Let's go back, Vishnu," said Mark. "We'll have to build a trap in order to catch a monkey. They move too fast for us."

Vishnu was reluctant to give up the chase. "There's a baby one," he whispered. "Look! I'll climb the tree."

But even the baby monkey got away from them.

Finally Vishnu agreed to go back to the clearing. As he led the way through the brush, he suddenly stopped. A strange look came over his face. "I can't find the trail," he said.

Mark wasn't sure what to do. If Vishnu, a boy of the jungle, was bewildered, they must be in trouble. For a moment they stood and looked around uncertainly. Then a noise in the bushes made them jump. Not waiting for Vishnu to lead the way, Mark bolted through the brush. His shirt caught on a thorn bush. He pulled away from the bush leaving a piece of his shirt behind.

Nothing mattered now but to get away from that noise in the bushes and find their way home. Tales of the dangers of the jungle flashed through his mind. Dad had warned him of what he might encounter if he ventured too far.

Frantically he ran and Vishnu ran after him, but they did not find the trail. Suddenly Mark stopped in alarm.

"Look, Vishnu!" he exclaimed. There on a thorn bush in front of them hung a scrap of his shirt.

"We've been going in circles!" he cried.

Vishnu nodded. His eyes were dark with fear. He looked up at the bits of sky he could see through the dense foliage, trying to determine the position of the sun. "We must find our way out before darkness falls," he said in a scared voice. "The spirits of the dead roam the forests at night."

Mark shivered a little as he thought about Vishnu's words. The spirits of the dead? No, that was only a superstition of the Campa people. But animals roamed the forests at night, fierce leopards and wildcats. Snakes were always around. He looked fearfully from his feet to the overhanging branches above him. To think they were lost in a place like this!

"What shall we do?" asked Vishnu in a hoarse whisper.

Mark knew there was only one thing to do—pray, pray that they find the trail or that somebody find them. Silently, with a pounding heart, he asked God to help them.

Suddenly Mark had an idea. If they left a trail

behind them they could be traced more easily. His shirt was already torn. If he tore off little bits of his shirt and dropped them as they went, rescuers would be more likely to find them.

Thanking God for giving him the idea, Mark began to leave little bits of his shirt behind him as he followed Vishnu through the forest. Sharp branches and thorns scratched their arms and legs. They were hungry, tired, and scared.

Suddenly Vishnu stopped. His practiced eye could tell that night was not far away. Darkness comes swiftly in the jungle. There is no twilight or dusk. They must find a place to spend the night.

"Why not climb a tree?" suggested Mark. "I'd feel safer off the ground, wouldn't you?"

Vishnu did not answer but numbly followed the missionary boy as he scrambled up a tree.

As they huddled closely together, Mark knew Vishnu was thinking about the spirits of the dead who were about to come out to terrify them. Mark wondered anxiously how many fierce animals could climb trees! "Jesus, help us," he prayed over and over again. He should never have gone into the forest with Vishnu. They had not intended to go so far. What must his parents be thinking? "Jesus, help us," he prayed again.

Darkness fell. Mark felt Vishnu shudder beside him. Mark knew why his friend was so afraid. His god was gone. He had nobody to pray to for protection now that the sun had set.

(to be continued)

695 words

When Darkness Falls

Part 3

The missionary boy Mark and his Campa friend Vishnu were lost in the jungle. Mark was afraid of the wild animals that might attack them. He prayed to God to help them. Vishnu was terrified of the spirits of the dead that he believed roamed about at night. He had no god to pray to for protection, because his god, the sun, was even then sinking in the west.

Darkness fell quickly. Mark felt Vishnu shudder beside him. Mark knew why his friend was so afraid. His god was gone. He had no protection now that the sun had set.

"Vishnu," he said, trying to sound brave, "the true God is with us. He doesn't leave us when the sun stops shining. He is with us in the darkness as well as in the light. He is not a part-time God, Vishnu."

"That's what your father told us at our reading lesson this morning," said Vishnu quietly.

Encouraged by Vishnu's words, Mark went on: "We don't have to be afraid of death if we believe in Him. We won't have to roam the forests at night after we die. Jesus will take us to a wonderful clearing in the sky to be with Him forever. We call it Heaven, and it's a happy, beautiful place."

Vishnu clutched Mark's arm. His ear, tuned to the sounds of the jungle, had heard something.

Mark felt prickly all over. What was it? A leopard? A wildcat? A slithering snake that swallowed deer and boys alive? Then he heard the wail piercing the night and making his blood run cold.

"There they are," said Vishnu in a hoarse whisper. "That's somebody's spirit wailing. It's coming to get us."

"Spirits don't wail," said Mark, remembering what his father had taught him. "Dad says it's a bird that makes that weird noise. Honest, Vishnu, it's a bird or something."

Vishnu was not convinced. "Sshh," he warned.

Mark looked out into the blackness but could see nothing. If there was a moon, the heavy foliage was hiding it from view. He reminded himself of what he told Vishnu: his god, the sun, left at night, but Mark's God didn't. Jesus said, "I am with you always," and that meant nighttime, too, even nighttime in the jungle.

Hearing a low rustle, Mark turned his head. A pair of eyes glowed in the darkness. For a minute he was almost hypnotized by the eyes that moved in a circle around them. His heart seemed to stop beating as he realized what was happening: they were being stalked by a wild animal! Any moment the animal might spring upon them.

Should they climb higher in the tree? Should they jump down and run? His mouth went dry. "Jesus, help us," he prayed desperately.

Suddenly another eye shone in the darkness, much brighter than the first two. Mark thought he would die of fright. Vishnu gripped his arm so hard it hurt. They waited tensely as the one-eyed monster came closer, crashing through the brush. They forgot the stalking animal in the face of this new terror.

An explosion! Vishnu screamed and would have fallen from the tree if Mark had not hung onto him. Suddenly Mark understood. The mysterious eye was none other than Dad's trusty flashlight. The explosion was his gun scaring off the animal stalking them.

The boys jumped down from the tree into the circle of rescuers below. The missionary hugged them both and then led them through the brush to the trail that would take them back to the clearing.

"How did you ever find us in the dark?" asked Mark as they made their way along the trail.

"My flashlight picked up

the bits of your shirt you had left. That was a good idea, son," said Dad.

"I think Jesus gave me the idea," Mark answered. "I asked Him to help us, and then I thought of it."

For a moment the only sounds were the night noises of the jungle and their own footsteps on the trail. Then Mark spoke again. "Dad, I'm glad Jesus isn't a part-time God. He isn't with us only when the sun is shining, but at night, too."

"Yes," agreed Dad, "we have a wonderful God. That's why we came to Peru, to tell the Campa people about Him."

"After tonight maybe Vishnu will believe, too," said Mark thoughtfully. "I should think he'd want a God that doesn't leave him at night."

They were at the end of the trail at last. The rescue-party men rushed forward to their welcome campfire, glad to be out of the dark jungle at last. Mark saw a light in the bamboo-palm house. He knew his mother had lit the kerosene lamp and was anxiously waiting for them.

As he ran to her he said a special thank you to his "full-time" God.

820 words

Girl of Siberia

Part 1

Note these words:

Vashchenko (vä·shĕn′kō)

harass: *to irritate, pester, torment*

atheist: *someone who believes there is no God*

perplexed: *confused*

refugee: *one who flees in search of safety*

plight: *a bad situation*

Lilia put her ear as close as possible to the radio set. One o'clock in the morning was too late for a twelve-year-old girl to stay up, but Mother and Father allowed her this privilege so that she could receive Bible teaching. All religious programs at that time were jammed by the Soviet government. Only late at night could they be heard.

Lilia knew what her family believed. Her father, Peter Vashchenko, had been in prison three times and once in a mental institution because of his religious beliefs and practices. Her parents had been harassed by the government in many ways; still they clung to their belief in God. Lilia realized that being Christians mattered more to them than anything else in the world. Next in importance to them was that their children share their faith.

Lilia did not fully understand how frustrated her parents were living in a country where it was against the law to be Christians. She often saw and heard her mother pray with tears streaming down her cheeks. After the prayer her mother smiled and was calm.

Lilia longed to learn her mother's secret. That is why she listened to the Christian programs late at night when she had a chance. Through them she came to know and love the Savior whom her parents loved and worshiped.

Because their children received only atheistic teaching in the public school in Siberia, the Vashchenkos took three of their girls out of school and taught them at home. The authorities declared this to be against the law. After many threats, the girls were kidnapped and taken to a boarding school in a distant city. There they were taught there is no God.

A worker at the school wondered why the girls were often crying, and found out from them what had happened. At great risk to herself, she notified Lilia's parents of the girls' whereabouts. Mr. and Mrs. Vashchenko took turns making the long trip to visit them, meeting them secretly in a graveyard.

Finally Lilia's father decided to leave the Soviet Union and take his family to a country where they would have freedom of religion. He made six trips to Moscow from their home in Siberia to get permission to leave the Soviet Union. They were long and expensive journeys.

The sixth time he took his family along. These determined people rushed past the Soviet guards and gained entrance into the American embassy.

A 17-year-old brother of Lilia's didn't make it. Seized by the guards, he was beaten, imprisoned, and finally sent back to Siberia.

The American officials in the U.S. embassy were perplexed as to what to do with the seven Siberians who had stormed their gates. The refugees sat in the embassy waiting room day after day, stretching out on the couches or on the floor at night to try to sleep. They dared not leave the building, because they knew, if they did, they would be put to death by their government as traitors.

After about two months of living in the waiting room, the Siberian family was given a very small apartment in the embassy basement, ten feet by sixteen. What a relief it was for them to have these crowded quarters. At last they had a little privacy, a stove to cook on, a refrigerator, a shower, two twin beds, a table, and a chair.

An embassy employee brought them food every

day. Lilia laughs when she remembers the first time they were served spaghetti. They thought the Parmesan cheese was soap for washing dishes!

Lilia lived with the six others in the basement apartment for five years! During the first three and a half years of that time they were allowed only fifteen minutes a day in the embassy courtyard for exercise. After that they could spend as much time in the courtyard as they liked.

The long waiting period was very hard for them. Although often perplexed, Lilia and her family never lost their faith in the Lord. They knew He was with them, but sometimes He seemed far away.

During the first three years they were permitted very few visitors. Later the rules changed and a number of famous people from the United States came to see them. A well-known author wrote their story so that people all over knew their plight.

(to be continued)

705 words

Girl of Siberia

Part 2

Note this word:
publicity: *information spread to the people*

Seeking religious freedom, Lilia's family spent five years as refugees in the U.S. embassy in Moscow.

While Lilia and her family were living in the U.S. embassy in Moscow, Christians in the free world were trying to help them. Students and teachers of a Christian university began campaigns for their freedom. They sent an appeal to President Reagan.

Finally, because of continued publicity and pressure from the United States government, the Soviets permitted the refugees, including all the other members of their family still in Siberia, to leave the Soviet Union. They were even allowed to take the family dog!

Arriving in the United States in 1983, the parents and younger children settled in the state of Washington, while the others scattered to Idaho, Missouri, Oregon, and California where they found opportunities for education, employment, and marriage.

Lilia went to school in Washington to learn English and finish her high school education. This took two years. After this she was awarded a scholarship and enrolled in a university. She was able to earn some money working at the university Russian department, correcting papers.

At first Lilia, while attending school, lived in an apartment with her sister. One day an American friend came to visit them. She was shocked to discover that the Russian girls had no furniture. She offered to move in with them and help them buy beds, a table, and chairs. After that they were much more comfortable.

Lilia found things in the United States very different from her own country. Our supermarkets with their brightly-colored packaged foods delighted as well as bewildered her. She was used to stores with bare shelves: perhaps one kind of fish, no meat, and not many other items.

Coffee was not for sale in Russia in those days, only a substitute. In the United States Lilia discovered there was not only plenty of coffee to be bought, but there was also a great variety of brands to choose from. Another thing that amazed her was the shelves and shelves of dog and cat food, something unheard of in the Soviet Union.

The greatest luxury of all, however, was the freedom she enjoyed. "I can go wherever I want," she said, "and nobody asks me any questions." She was free to worship God and attend church as she pleased with no government regulations or punishment.

One thing about the United States puzzled and disappointed Lilia, however. She had imagined that because of freedom of religion in the United States, everyone would choose to be a Christian, but she found out this was not the case. The majority of people in our country do not know God or follow His ways.

Lilia was challenged to be strong in her faith even if many people around her were walking away from God instead of with Him.

Today Lilia is a happy wife and the mother of a daughter named Tiffany.

Lilia's father passed away from cancer in October of 1985. His family will be forever grateful to him for what he endured in bringing them to freedom. Now their children can grow up in a country where it is not a crime to be a Christian, to read the Bible, or to teach children about God. Lilia is determined that her father's sacrifice for her will not be in vain.

Conditions in Lilia's homeland have changed somewhat since she and her family lived there. There are churches now that people can attend without being punished.

These churches are very few, however, considering the large population of the country. Many towns do not have even one place for Christians to gather for worship. A great number of people have not yet heard the message of Jesus.

There is also much poverty in Lilia's homeland. This is especially felt during the long, cold winters. Adequate medical care is lacking also. Concerned Christians from the United States and other countries send money, food, clothing, and medical aid when possible. The greatest need of all is for more pastors and missionaries to teach the people about the true God Whom they were forbidden to worship for so long.

The Soviet Union has a new name now. It is called the Commonwealth of Independent States, C.I.S. for short. Lilia's homeland needs our prayers very much. Ask God to send missionaries and pastors to this needy place. Maybe someday He will send you!

735 words

Happy Ending

Note these words:

Junichi (jo͞on·ē·chē) Iesu (ē·ĕ·so͞o) amputate: *to cut off*

kami-shibai (kä·mē·shē·bä·ē): *a portable box used in telling visualized stories*

Junichi jumped off his bicycle and leaned it against a pine tree. He ran over to where a group of boys and girls were gathered.

"Must be a kami-shibai," he murmured to himself as he hurried eagerly to join the group. He loved the stories of the evil creatures that the kami-shibai men told as they showed the children the large colored pictures.

Junichi was surprised to see not a kami-shibai man, but two ladies in the midst of the boys and girls. They were showing pictures, too, but they were not about evil creatures. They were telling the children about a person named Jesus, Who they said was the Son of the one true God.

Like other children in Japan, Junichi had been taught that there are many gods. He had bowed before the ugly idols in the temple and offered rice to his ancestors. He had always feared the gods.

These ladies were talking about a God Who loved children; His name was Jesus.

Although Junichi was only eight years old and seemingly a happy boy, down in the bottom of his heart there was sadness. He was sad because his father, who was kind to him when he was sober, came home drunk so often. Then he was not kind to Junichi, his mother, or his little sister. Then Junichi was afraid of his father.

"All of us are sinners," the lady was saying, "and no matter how strong we are, we cannot get free from our sin by ourselves."

Junichi nodded in agreement. His father could not stop drinking rice wine even though he had tried many times.

"The one true God sent His son, Jesus, to save us from our sins," the teacher went on. "He died on the cross so we could be free and someday go to Heaven to live with Him forever. He will take your sins away, too, if you believe on Him and ask Him to."

Then the lady did a strange thing. She told the

children to bow their heads, close their eyes, and fold their hands. When everyone was quiet she explained to the children that even though they could not see Him, they could talk to Jesus, and she did.

Junichi was very thoughtful as he got on his bicycle and rode home. "Jesus," he whispered, "I don't understand about you, but please help me. Take my sins away, too." After Junichi had prayed to Jesus, he felt good inside. Maybe this Jesus could help his father stop drinking rice wine and they could have a happy home.

The next day Junichi eagerly started off again to go to hear more about Jesus. The ladies had promised that they would hold another class out under the trees, and he did not want to miss it.

Junichi was so full of his own thoughts that he did not remember the railroad tracks ahead of him. He came right up to them without stopping to look. Around the bend a fast train was coming. The conductor saw the boy and tried to stop, but it was too late. When the train finally screeched to a halt, Junichi was lying crumpled beside the track, one leg crushed and his head bleeding.

Junichi suffered very much as the doctors had to amputate his leg below the knee. In his suffering, instead of calling for his father or mother he called out "Iesu! Iesu!" which means "Jesus" in Japanese. His parents were puzzled. Who was this Jesus?

The ladies who had taught Junichi about Jesus came to visit him at the hospital. Then his parents understood.

Everyone said it was a miracle that Junichi had not been killed. Day by day he grew stronger, and finally he was able to go home.

A few weeks later his father took him to Sunday school on the back of his bicycle. Junichi listened eagerly to the stories of Jesus. He went nearly every Sunday, either on the back of his father's bicycle or on the bus when the weather was bad. Sometimes his father stayed for the church service.

Everyone felt sorry for Junichi hobbling around on his crutches, but his face always looked bright and happy. One day when he went to Sunday school, he had two legs again. One was an artificial leg. Soon he learned to walk without his crutches and even ride his bicycle. He is praying that his mother, father, and little sister will soon learn to know Jesus, too.

755 words

Choco Calls

Part 1

Note these words:

Choco (chə·kō′) Cobija (kō·bē′hä)

falter: *to stumble over words, to speak with hesitation*

Choco stopped and looked around him in bewilderment. Where were the rubber trees, anyway? He thought that by now he would have found three or four of them and have his tin full of liquid rubber. But he had not found even one!

Choco cast a worried glance at the sky. Through the lacy foliage of the jungle trees he could see that the sun was not directly overhead. It was past noon. Choco's stomach told him so, too. He had been so eager to go on his hunt for rubber that he had forgotten to ask Mama for some food to take along.

Dejectedly, the Bolivian boy swung himself onto the low branch of a friendly tree and looked about him. A frightening thought kept pestering him, making a worried frown crease his brown forehead. Was he lost? Lost in the jungle?

Choco had been lying asleep in his hammock in the hut that morning when Papa's voice had awakened him. Choco had not opened his eyes, for then Mama probably would have sent him for water. He had only half-listened to what his father was saying.

"Mama, I slept hardly at all last night. I am so miserable I could die!"

Choco had pricked up his ears when he heard these strange words from his usually happy-go-lucky father. He had even opened his eyes to look. He had never seen Papa look so sad before.

Mama had only stirred the rice and had not answered. She had looked worried, too. Whatever could be wrong?

"I must go to Cobija to talk to the missionary. Maybe he can help me. I can't go on like this."

The man had lifted troubled eyes to his wife. Choco had closed his eyes quickly. It had bothered him to see Papa look so sad. Why must he go to the missionary? Would he ask him for money? Didn't Papa have any money left to buy food? If not, he should go to the jungle to look for rubber instead of to the missionary!

Papa had said good-bye to Mama and hurried out of the hut. Slowly a plan had formed in Choco's mind as he lay quietly in his hammock. He would take his father's tin can and go to tap the rubber trees. Tonight he would smoke it over the fire, turning the stick round and round until he had a big ball for Papa to sell. Then Papa wouldn't be sad anymore.

Choco had jumped out of his hammock and run to get water even before Mama asked him.

After his breakfast of rice and mashed bananas, Choco had grabbed one of his Papa's tin cans and started for the forest. He had tramped around for hours but had not seen even one rubber tree to tap.

Now Choco shivered a little and drew his ragged shirt closer around him. It was beginning to rain. He looked unhappily at the empty tin can. He had no rubber to bring to Papa, and besides, he did not know where he was. He was lost!

Lost! That's what the missionary had talked about when he visited their village a few days ago. Choco could remember his words. "We have all gone astray in sin. We are like lost sheep, unable to find our way to God and His beautiful home. But there is One who wants to find you and set your feet on the path to Heaven. That is Jesus Who died on the cross to pay for your sins."

Choco felt in the pocket of his old black pants for the little slip of paper with the verse that the missionary had given him.

"For whosoever shall call upon the name of the Lord shall be saved," he read slowly.

Choco dangled his legs

over the branch and looked thoughtfully around him at the dense jungle foliage. The missionary had urged the villagers to call upon the Lord Jesus and ask Him to save them. Then they wouldn't be lost from God anymore, he said. They would be His children and on their way to His home in the skies.

Choco frowned thoughtfully. If he called on the name of the Lord would He show him the way out of the jungle? He didn't care about finding rubber trees now. If only he could find his way home!

Choco closed his eyes as he had seen the missionary do when he talked to God. "Dear Jesus," he faltered. "I'm lost in the jungle. Please help me to find my way home."

(to be continued)

765 words

Choco Calls

Part 2

When Choco thought his father needed money, he decided to help by getting rubber for him to sell. Instead of helping, Choco is lost in the jungle.

Choco, lost in the jungle, had decided to call upon the missionary's God for help to find his way home. Jumping down from the tree where he had taken refuge, he plunged through the underbrush. The missionary's God would help him. He would find his way home.

After a long time of pushing his way through the forest, Choco stopped and looked around him. That tree—it looked familiar. He saw something white on the ground. He looked closer. It was his slip of paper. He was back to the place from which he had started!

Close to tears, Choco picked up the piece of paper and crumpled it angrily. The missionary's God had not helped him after all. He was as lost as ever!

Fear gripped the boy's heart. Anxiously he eyed the sun filtering through the branches. What would he do when the sun set and darkness fell? Choco shivered. He had no desire to be out in the jungle alone in the dark. What about the wild animals that prowled in the darkness, and the snakes? He *must* find his way home. Choco turned and began to run wildly, but suddenly he stopped. What had Papa said about being lost in the jungle? "Don't run, because you will only go in circles. Find an anthorn and call. Somebody will hear you and come."

Choco looked eagerly under the tall plants. Sure enough, there were anthills and buried among them, long tubelike things. Carefully he broke one off, put it to his lips, and began to call.

Out of breath he paused for a moment. The words of the missionary's verse came back to him: "Whosoever shall call upon the name of the Lord shall be saved." What if nobody came to rescue Choco and he died in the jungle? He wouldn't be able to go to God's heavenly home, because he didn't know the way there, either. The missionary said only Jesus could take him there.

For a moment Choco forgot about being lost in the jungle. He bowed his head. "Jesus, please save me. Let me walk Your path to Your heavenly house."

Choco felt happy as he raised the anthorn to his lips to call again. He had asked Jesus to save him, and now, even though he was still lost in the jungle, he was not lost to God anymore.

Choco jumped nervously when he heard a rustling in the brush behind him. Then he dropped his anthorn and ran forward eagerly.

"Papa, you came! You found me!"

"Yes," answered Papa. "You did right to call. I was on the trail coming home from the missionary's house when I heard calls of distress. I did not know it was my own son."

Choco suddenly remembered why he had come to the forest. He held out the empty tin can to his father. "Papa, I came looking for rubber trees. I wanted to find a whole canful of rubber for you to smoke and sell. You looked so sad this morning. But I couldn't find the rubber trees. I—" his voice trailed off.

Papa patted Choco's shoulder. Choco looked at him and noticed that he did not look sad anymore. In fact, he had never seen Papa look so happy. He stared at his father.

"Yes, I was sad," Papa answered, "but now I am glad. You see, I have talked to the missionary, and he told me how I could be saved from my sin. I called upon the Lord Jesus, and He has saved me."

"Whosoever shall call upon the name of the Lord shall be saved," recited Choco with awe. "It is written right here on my paper." The boy eagerly pulled the crumpled slip out of his pocket.

"Ah, my boy, I cannot read, but you shall read for me," said Papa. "See, I bought a book from the missionary, a New Testament, he called it. It is God's Word. Tonight we shall not smoke rubber. Tonight we shall learn about the road to Heaven. Come, let us go quickly."

Choco followed his father through the brush to the path. How easy it seemed now to find the way since he had a guide. How glad he was he had thought of calling through the anthorn and that Papa had found him. He was glad he had called upon Jesus, too, because now God had found him and he belonged to Him.

770 words

Marie's Dream

Part 1

Marie wanted to be a missionary to China from the time she was a small girl. Her mother told her about the girl babies in China who were not wanted by their parents. Those who kept their baby girls bound their feet so they would be small and dainty. Marie determined that when she grew up she would go and tell them about Jesus.

Marie's parents had immigrated to the United States from Norway. They eventually settled on a farm in North Dakota. One afternoon her father and older brother were cutting hay out in the field. Marie's mother sent her and her sister out to the field with lunch for the workers.

"Here is your coffee, Papa," said Marie, and stepped right into the path of the sickle which was being pulled by two horses. Marie felt agonizing pain as the sharp sickle cut through her leg. Her injured leg had to be amputated.

Marie suffered a long time from the amputation because the doctor had not amputated it correctly. Her leg did not heal, so she had to have a second operation. Contrary to the doctor's expectations, the second surgery was successful and Marie was finally able to get around by using crutches. Later she was fitted with an artificial leg.

As a teenager Marie had many friends, but most of them weren't Christians. She soon began to forget about God and think only of having fun. She gave up her dreams of going to China as a missionary. All this time she was not happy. She felt that God was angry with her, and she was doomed forever.

One night she had a dream of Jesus coming to get her. In her dream He said, "Marie, your sins are forgiven; only believe." She awoke full of joy, but Satan was at hand to discourage her. "It was only a dream," he reminded her.

Marie reached for her Bible. As she opened it her eyes fell on Luke 7:48: "And He said unto her, Thy sins are forgiven." Marie knew then that God had accepted her. Immediately she began to witness to her ungodly friends, and some of them also came to Jesus to be saved.

When Marie returned to the Lord, her call to missionary work in China was renewed. One day she told her parents that she felt God wanted her in China.

Her father burst out laughing when she told him of her desire. He reminded her that she was not strong and had only one leg. He said she should never mention her desire to go to China to anyone, for they would only make fun of her.

Marie felt sad when her father ridiculed the idea of her going to China. She knew that if God wanted her to go, He would make it possible in spite of all the hindrances.

One Sunday, to Marie's great joy, a missionary from China came to speak at their church. After the service she had a chance to talk to the missionary lady.

The missionary did not think Marie was foolish for wanting to go to China. She assured her that if it was God's will, He would make it happen. She also told her about a training school where she could go to become prepared for missionary work. Marie learned a great deal during those days, but she was not encouraged to go to China. In fact, the leader of the training school told her it was wrong for her to even consider such a thing.

Marie hardly slept the night she was told that. How was it she felt so strongly she must go to China if God did not want her to go?

After attending the training school, Marie enrolled in her church's Bible school. Marie was told again that she should not think of going to China because of her frail health and artificial leg.

How surprised Marie was when she heard later that the mission board had changed their mind and approved of her going. A group of missionaries were leaving for China in five weeks, and she was asked to go with them.

Overjoyed, Marie started making preparations for the trip. She decided to leave her crutches at home. The Lord would help her walk without them (and He did).

After the difficult good-byes to family and friends had been said, Marie traveled with the other missionary candidates to British Columbia where they boarded a ship for China. Marie's dream was coming true at last!

(to be continued)

760 words

Marie's Dream

Part 2

Note these words:
Hankow (hăng·kou) Tsaoyng (sou·yŭng)
Werdal (wẽr·dôl′)

Marie's life-long dream has been to go to China as a missionary even though she is not strong and has an artificial leg. After facing discouragement from her father and Christian leaders, Marie is finally on her way to China.

Marie was so seasick on the ship to China that she decided she never wanted to cross the ocean again. Little did she know that she would cross it nine more times in her lifetime.

The missionaries finally arrived in Shanghai where they left the ship. From there they traveled by steamer up the Yangtse River to Hankow, a trip of four days. A missionary met them there and helped them get their papers in order. They also purchased such necessary items as cork hats and mosquito nets. From Hankow they traveled by train. The last lap of their journey was by sedan chair. Strong men carried the chairs by poles on their shoulders.

The Chinese were curious about these strange pale-faced creatures. Most of them had never seen foreigners before. They wanted to look at the feet of the women and laughed to see how big they were compared to theirs. They wanted to see if their ears were punctured for earrings and how they put up their hair. In the inns where they spent the night, they were afraid the mob would break down the door of their room, so eager were they to see the "foreign devils" as they called them.

At last they arrived at Tsaoyang and were greeted not only by the missionaries but by the Chinese Christians as well. Marie was in her glory. She was a missionary to China at last!

Marie could say only three words in Chinese: "we," "come," and "go." Eagerly she began to study the language. She could hardly wait to tell the Chinese people about Jesus. She studied so hard the missionaries worried about her becoming sick. When she was able to make up some sentences, she went out to try them on the Chinese. If they understood her she was delighted; if they did not, she went back to study harder.

Marie quickly discovered that missionary life in China was not only difficult but sometimes dangerous as well. The people to whom they had come were very superstitious. If something good happened to them, they believed the missionaries had brought them good fortune. If disaster struck, they blamed the missionaries and started a riot.

Also dangerous were the bandits roaming the countryside, sometimes in large bands. They would come into a town looting, stealing, and even killing. More than once the missionaries had to flee into the countryside to escape from the bandits, but God always protected them.

Marius Werdal, a single missionary among them,

needed a wife. Whom would he choose? There were several single women. To everyone's surprise, he chose Marie, even though she was weak and had only one leg. Marie, confident that God was leading them, was happy to marry Marius.

The next stage of Marie's life included not only teaching the Chinese, but motherhood as well. This tiny, frail woman eventually gave birth to six children: one girl and five boys. Four of them became missionaries when they grew to adulthood.

After 21 years in China, the Werdals came back to the United States and settled down in Ferndale, Washington. They believed their missionary work was finished, but God had other plans for them. After five years at home the mission board asked them to return to China. In spite of poor health, they willingly went out again, trusting the Lord to help them.

It was at this time that war with Japan broke out in China. The missionaries had to dig tunnels to take refuge in when the planes came thundering overhead. They used the church bell to warn the people of coming danger.

The city where the missionaries lived was bombed many times. They kept on with their daily Bible studies for the Christians but were often interrupted by the bombs. They were glad they were there to encourage the Chinese Christians.

Finally things became so dangerous the American Consul sent word that the missionaries must return to the United States. On the way to the seacoast to board the ship, Marius became very ill and died. Marie was heartbroken at first until the

Lord assured her that it was His will that Marius go to be with Him. She knew he was happy in Heaven and was comforted.

The weary missionaries were able to board a plane for India and from there get on a crowded ship to take them back to the United States.

Marie Werdal went back to China one more time, accompanied by her daughter Mildred, her son Philip, and his family. This time it was the Communists who caused them trouble and finally made it necessary for them to return to the United States.

Marie lived to be over 90 years of age, a blessing to her family and others. She had experienced much trouble during her life but had learned to praise God in it all. She proved what Paul wrote in 1 Corinthians 1:27, "God hath chosen the weak things of the world to confound the things which are mighty."

880 words

Reading Record and Quizzes

Reading Record

Selection	Words/Minute	Grade
God Was Taking Care of Andre	__________	_______
The Most Important Lesson—Part 1	__________	_______
The Most Important Lesson—Part 2	__________	_______
The Most Important Lesson—Part 3	__________	_______
Village Boy of Mexico—Part 1	__________	_______
Village Boy of Mexico—Part 2	__________	_______
A Testing Time—Part 1	__________	_______
A Testing Time—Part 2	__________	_______
A Testing Time—Part 3	__________	_______
Anatole's Adventure	__________	_______
Yochi's Front Teeth—Part 1	__________	_______
Yochi's Front Teeth—Part 2	__________	_______
Detour to Joy	__________	_______
The Domino Effect	__________	_______
Rescue Two Ways	__________	_______
The Bread, Cake, and Candy Man	__________	_______
A Bulldog, a Goat, and an Elephant	__________	_______
Street Boy	__________	_______
When Darkness Falls—Part 1	__________	_______
When Darkness Falls—Part 2	__________	_______
When Darkness Falls—Part 3	__________	_______
Girl of Siberia—Part 1	__________	_______
Girl of Siberia—Part 2	__________	_______

Selection	Words/Minute	Grade
Happy Ending	______	______
Choco Calls—Part 1	______	______
Choco Calls—Part 2	______	______
Marie's Dream—Part 1	______	______
Marie's Dream—Part 2	______	______

Quiz 1
God Was Taking Care of Andre
Page 2

_________ %

_________ wpm

Name ______________________________

Directions: *Circle or write the correct answer.*

1. Andre Dwina lives in __?__ .
   a. Bombay, India
   b. Paris, France
   c. Peking, China
   d. Chad, Africa

2. After he was converted to Christ, Andre __?__ .
   a. went to college
   b. became a teacher
   c. attended several short-term Bible schools
   d. built stone church buildings

3. Soldiers were going to kill Andre because __?__ .
   a. he would not pay his taxes
   b. he was a missionary from the United States
   c. he wanted to take over the government
   d. he would not deny Christ even when threatened with death

4. When nobody wanted to shoot Andre, they decided __?__ .
   a. to send him home
   b. to punish him and let him go
   c. to make him a slave
   d. to bury him alive

5. Andre's executioners fled when __?__ .
   a. Andre's friends came to the rescue
   b. their national leader was killed
   c. Andre began fighting them
   d. a fierce storm arose

6. True or False: Andre was able to keep on preaching because he was clever.

Number of words: 400 ÷ ____ Minutes reading time = rate ____

Quiz 2
The Most Important Lesson Part 1
Page 5

Name ________________________________

__________ %

__________ wpm

Directions: *Circle or write the correct answer.*

1. Tomiko was a girl of __?__ .
   a. Japan
   b. India
   c. the United States
   d. Korea

2. What did Tomiko want to do when she got home from school?

   ____

3. Tomiko's parents wanted her to study English from an American because __?__ .
   a. it would make their neighbors envious
   b. it was not expensive
   c. she would learn proper pronunciation
   d. it would keep her out of mischief

4. When her mother told her about the English conversation class, Tomiko __?__ .
   a. was enthusiastic
   b. refused to go
   c. made a big fuss
   d. went reluctantly

5. Tomiko's parents had not learned English from Americans when they were children because __?__ .
   a. they could never have afforded it
   b. it was against their religious beliefs to learn English
   c. there were no Americans in their town
   d. their parents would not allow it

6. Father insisted that their people needed to be educated in order to __?__ .
   a. be famous
   b. be rich
   c. keep up with the changing world
   d. be proud of themselves

Number of words: 425 ÷ _____ Minutes reading time = rate _____

Name ______________________________

Quiz 3
The Most Important Lesson Part 2
Page 8

__________ %

__________ wpm

Directions: *Circle or write the correct answer.*

1. The English class was held in __?__ .
   - **a.** a schoolroom
   - **b.** the teacher's home
   - **c.** a Christian church
   - **d.** a hotel room

2. The Japanese students had a hard time pronouncing __?__ .
   - **a.** ch
   - **b.** dr
   - **c.** pl
   - **d.** th

3. After the lesson, they had a chapel time where a Japanese teacher told them __?__ .
   - **a.** tales of old Japan
   - **b.** funny stories about the United States
   - **c.** stories of Jesus
   - **d.** fairy tales

4. How did Tomiko feel about her English class after that first time?
   - **a.** bored
   - **b.** fascinated
   - **c.** angry
   - **d.** uninterested

5. What event was Tomiko looking forward to?

   ____

6. True or False: Tomiko didn't tell her father about the chapel time because she was afraid he might embarrass her by coming with her the next week.

Number of words: 470 ÷ _____ Minutes reading time = rate _____

Name ________________________________

Quiz 4
The Most Important Lesson Part 3
Page 10

________ %

________ wpm

Directions: *Circle or write the correct answer.*

1. Today, the majority of Japanese celebrate Christmas by __?__ .
   a. shopping and decorating
   b. worshiping Jesus
   c. playing games
   d. traveling

2. The colored ribbons of the Gospel Nut explained __?__ .
   a. an interesting color scheme
   b. the history of the walnut
   c. God's way of salvation
   d. the worship of old Japan

3. The black ribbon represented __?__ .
   a. the devil
   b. sin and darkness
   c. the earth
   d. velvet

4. The red ribbon represented __?__ .
   a. Jesus' death on the cross
   b. Christmas lights
   c. gaiety
   d. gift giving

5. True or False: The white ribbon showed what happens to our hearts when Jesus cleanses them.

6. The gold ribbon reminds us of ______________________________ .

7. True or False: Tomiko decided to tell her parents about Jesus because she wanted them to go to Heaven someday, too.

Number of words: 510 ÷ ______ Minutes reading time = rate ______

Quiz 5
Village Boy of Mexico Part 1
Page 13

__________ %

__________ wpm

Name ____________________________________

Directions: *Circle or write the correct answer.*

1. The village boy Manuel envied the Mexicans in the cities because they were __?__ .
   - **a.** rich
   - **b.** jolly
   - **c.** strong
   - **d.** smart

2. Manuel's father thought Manuel should __?__ .
   - **a.** go to school
   - **b.** work in the fields
   - **c.** work for the Mexicans
   - **d.** help his mother

3. True or False: Even though Manuel's father was poor, he always had plenty to eat.

4. Check the three things below that surprised Manuel about the missionary family.
   - ___ The missionary wife was so tall.
   - ___ The missionary wife stood when she cooked.
   - ___ The missionary wife sat down with her husband while they ate.
   - ___ The missionaries closed their eyes before they ate.

5. Manuel was interested in the American man because he
   - **a.** did not take a nap in the afternoon.
   - **b.** did not dress as the village men did.
   - **c.** did not get drunk and beat his wife.
   - **d.** ate strange kinds of food.

6. What did the missionary hire Manuel to teach him?

   ____

7. True or False: Manuel was bored with this job.

Number of words: 485 ÷ _____ Minutes reading time = rate _____

Quiz 6
Village Boy of Mexico Part 2
Page 16

Name ________________________________

______ %

______ wpm

Directions: *Circle or write the correct answer.*

1. Manuel had a question about something concerning his gods and the missionary's God. What was it?

   ____

2. To find out if his family's gods were real, Manuel __?__ .
   a. talked to them and demanded an answer
   b. knocked one over
   c. stuck one with a needle
   d. asked his father

3. When Manuel discovered his gods were only lifeless idols, he __?__ .
   a. decided to worship the missionary's God
   b. threw the family gods down the mountainside
   c. did not tell anyone
   d. burst out laughing

4. The result of this action was that Manuel __?__ .
   a. got a terrible whipping from his father
   b. convinced his parents that the missionary's God was the true one
   c. had to leave home
   d. had to work harder than ever in the fields

5. True or False: Manuel's dream to go to school never came true.

6. True or False: Eventually, Manuel learned to speak several languages besides his own.

7. Manuel spent his life __?__ .
   a. gaining riches for himself
   b. traveling around the world
   c. helping his people learn about the true God
   d. being a politician in Mexico

Number of words: 515 ÷ ______ Minutes reading time = rate ______

Name ______________________________

Quiz 7
A Testing Time
Part 1
Page 19

________ %

________ wpm

Directions: *Circle or write the correct answer.*

1. True or False: The Mathews family had been invited by the church to come to Hwangyuan and had been given permission by the government.

2. True or False: When the Mathews family arrived in Hwangyuan, they were warmly welcomed by the Chinese Christians.

3. The missionaries were given __?__ .
   a. a fine house to live in
   b. only two small rooms to live in
   c. permission to live in the church
   d. a large apartment in a huge apartment building

4. After Arthur Mathews had rented a house and fixed it up as a clinic, __?__ .
   a. he began medical work there
   b. he was congratulated by the government
   c. a Chinese troop took it over
   d. it burned down before he could use it

5. The Chinese Christians did not associate closely with the missionaries because they __?__ .
   a. were jealous of them
   b. were afraid of their Communist overlords
   c. did not like them
   d. were too busy

6. True or False: The missionaries decided to apply for exit permits because their presence was endangering the Christians.

7. True or False: After reading this story, we realize that missionaries in China have always enjoyed freedom of religion.

Number of words: 510 ÷ ____ Minutes reading time = rate ____

Quiz 8
A Testing Time
Part 2
Page 22

_________ %

_________ wpm

Name ______________________________

Directions: *Circle or write the correct answer.*

1. When the authorities told the Mathews they could leave China, they __?__ .
   a. were sad
   b. went into hiding
   c. sold their belongings
   d. planned a party to say good-bye to all their friends

2. More than ________ years passed before they were allowed to leave.

3. The greatest difficulty the Mathews experienced at this time was __?__.
   a. getting money to buy what they needed
   b. getting the Chinese people to attend their services
   c. staying healthy
   d. hiding from the Communist soldiers

4. True or False: The Mathews often did not receive their money on time because Christians in the homeland kept forgetting to send it.

5. The greatest lesson they learned at this time was
   a. to spend their money wisely.
   b. to make tasty meals from plants growing around their village.
   c. to trust God and thank Him no matter what happened.
   d. to speak the Chinese language fluently.

6. True or False: The missionaries became angry with God for allowing them to go through these troubles.

7. Circle the things God wants to do for us through troubles.
   a. make us angry
   b. teach us patience
   c. teach us to trust him
   d. give us money

Number of words: 550 ÷ _____ Minutes reading time = rate _____

Name ______________________________

Quiz 9
A Testing Time
Part 3
Page 25

________ %

________ wpm

Directions: *Circle or write the correct answer.*

1. When Mrs. Mathews had no money to buy her daughter a birthday gift, she __?__ .
   a. picked pretty flowers for Lilah
   b. gave Lilah her own favorite necklace
   c. made Lilah a doll from old material
   d. made Lilah a delicious birthday cake

2. Who did God send to visit Lilah as a special treat on her birthday?

   ____

3. The authorities permitted Mrs. Mathews and Lilah to leave, but not Mr. Mathews because they said __?__ .
   a. he was a Communist
   b. he was a criminal
   c. the people needed him
   d. he owed tax money

4. When the authorities permitted only Mrs. Mathews and Lilah to leave China, Mr. Mathews __?__ .
   a. was angry
   b. kept trusting God
   c. was afraid
   d. told his wife and daughter not to go without him

5. True or False: When the Christians in the homeland wrote that they were encouraged by the Mathews' testimony, Arthur knew that God had a purpose for everything that had happened.

6. True or False: After the policeman picked Arthur up in the police vehicle and told him he could leave, Arthur had no more trouble reaching Hong Kong and his family.

7. This story teaches us that __?__ .
   a. serving Christ is not worth the pain
   b. you will never have problems if you become a missionary
   c. you will have many physical problems if you serve Christ
   d. you can trust God to do what is best for you

Number of words: 550 ÷ ____ Minutes reading time = rate ____

Quiz 10
Anatole's Adventure
Page 28

_________ %

_________ wpm

Name ______________________________

Directions: Circle or write the correct answer.

1. True or False: Anatole lived in the part of the C.I.S. known as the Ukraine.
2. True or False: Because Anatole was a brilliant student, he was praised by his teachers.
3. Why was Anatole harassed at school? ____________________

   ____
4. When Anatole became discouraged and joined the Communists, he __?__ .
   - **a.** was ridiculed
   - **b.** was made a sergeant in the army
   - **c.** got into trouble
   - **d.** lost his money
5. As a Communist, Anatole __?__ .
   - **a.** was happy and fulfilled
   - **b.** was very unhappy
   - **c.** had no friends
   - **d.** had peace in his heart
6. When Anatole returned to God, he __?__ .
   - **a.** continued in the army
   - **b.** opened a business
   - **c.** became a pastor
   - **d.** went to the United States
7. A friend from the United States visited Anatole and helped him buy __?__ .
   - **a.** a house
   - **b.** a bike
   - **c.** an airplane
   - **d.** a car
8. Giving to others is __?__ .
   - **a.** unnecessary
   - **b.** a privilege
   - **c.** stupid
   - **d.** painful

Number of words: 535 ÷ ____ Minutes reading time = rate ____

Quiz 11
Yochi's Front Teeth
Part 1
Page 31

________ %

________ wpm

Name ______________________________

Directions: *Circle or write the correct answer.*

1. What was Yochi so afraid of? ________________

   ____

2. Vietnamese boys went through this ritual when they had lived __?__.
   a. 10 summers
   b. 12 summers
   c. 15 summers
   d. 13 summers

3. Vietnamese boys had their teeth sawed off so that they would __?__.
   a. learn to endure pain
   b. not act wild and fierce like animals
   c. look ugly
   d. learn to face their fears

4. Why did Yochi go to see his grandmother rather than play with the other boys?
   a. He didn't like to play.
   b. He was too troubled to play.
   c. He would rather work.

5. True or False: Grandmother said it was necessary for Yochi to have his teeth sawed off so he could get a wife someday.

6. Who did Yochi see coming down the trail toward the vine bridge?
   a. Communist soldiers.
   b. a group of hunters.
   c. white-skinned men.

7. Yochi thought these strange visitors were __?__.
   a. clumsy
   b. handsome
   c. fierce

8. Where did Yochi go to watch the strange visitors?

   ____

Number of words: 530 ÷ _____ Minutes reading time = rate _____

Quiz 12
Yochi's Front Teeth
Part 2
Page 34

_________ %

_________ wpm

Name ______________________________

Directions: *Circle or write the correct answer.*

1. When Yochi saw the white people coming near his village, he _?_.
   - **a.** ran to meet them
   - **b.** stayed in the banyan tree where he was
   - **c.** ran back to the village
   - **d.** hid behind a rock until they passed

2. True or False: When Yochi saw the white men close up, he discovered they, too, had their teeth sawed off.

3. The missionary taught the people that _?_.
   - **a.** the tooth sawing was necessary
   - **b.** the teeth should be pulled out instead of sawed
   - **c.** Jesus can take away wildness and badness
   - **d.** sawed teeth helped them to be strong and brave

4. Who decided that Yochi did not have to have his teeth sawed?

   ____

5. Grandmother was worried that if Yochi's teeth were not sawed, he would _?_.
   - **a.** not be respected in the village
   - **b.** not get a wife
   - **c.** not be a real man
   - **d.** be driven out of the village

6. True or False: Yochi's father said that Yochi should have a Christian wife.

7. Yochi and his father called the missionaries' God the God of

   ____.

Number of words: 660 ÷ _____ Minutes reading time = rate _____

Quiz 13
Detour to Joy
Page 37

______ %
______ wpm

Name ____________________

Directions: *Circle or write the correct answer.*

1. Pasha's family was going to Siberia _?_.
   a. as prisoners
   b. to buy land cheap
   c. for a vacation
   d. on a business trip

2. What happened to Pasha's parents on the way to Siberia?

   ____

3. When Pasha ran away from the orphanage he was _?_.
   a. discovered and taken back
   b. carried off to Africa
   c. given a job on a railroad
   d. found by a robber gang

4. True or False: Pasha learned to steal and kill.

5. When Pasha and a friend found a Bible, what were they going to do with it at first?
   a. use it for cigarette papers
   b. keep their money hidden in it
   c. use it to start a fire
   d. sell it to a minister

6. What did they end up doing with the Bible? ______

   ____

7. Circle two results of their Bible reading.
   a. They became Christians.
   b. They escaped from the police.
   c. They gave themselves up to the police.

8. True or False: Pasha never saw his sister again.

Number of words: 570 ÷ ____ Minutes reading time = rate ____

Quiz 14
The Domino Effect
Page 40

______ %

______ wpm

Name ______________________

Directions: *Circle or write the correct answer.*

1. Sumiko and the other characters in this story suffered from __?__.
   a. cancer **c.** influenza
   b. tuberculosis **d.** diphtheria

2. Sumiko had heard about Jesus from __?__.
   a. her parents **c.** a missionary
   b. her doctor **d.** a neighbor

3. When able, Sumiko spent time at the hospital __?__.
   a. crocheting doilies **c.** painting pictures
   b. reading novels **d.** witnessing about Jesus

4. Mr. Saito, also a patient, had been __?__.
   a. a scientist **c.** a doctor
   b. an army officer **d.** a teacher

5. Mr. Saito became a Christian __?__.
   a. after he attended the memorial service of the girl he loved
   b. when he became an old man
   c. when he became very ill
   d. when an earthquake shattered the hospital

6–8. Write down in order the domino effect in this story starting with the missionary. Some of the blanks are filled in for you.

Here are the names to help you: the missionary, Mr. Saito, many others, Onuma, Sumiko.

<u>The missionary</u> won ________________, who won

<u>Onuma</u>, who won ________________, who

won ______________________.

Number of words: 605 ÷ _____ Minutes reading time = rate _____

Quiz 15
Rescued Two Ways
Page 43

__________ %

__________ wpm

Name ______________________________

Directions: *Circle or write the correct answer.*

1. The African boy Kaboo _?_.
   a. was buried by an enemy tribe
   b. was taken hostage by an enemy tribe
   c. ran away from his home
   d. became lost in the forest

2. Kaboo's captors intended to _?_.
   a. burn him
   b. shoot him
   c. make him a slave
   d. let ants eat him alive

3. When Kaboo escaped from his captors he _?_.
   a. congratulated himself
   b. thought he was lucky
   c. knew some great God had helped him
   d. thanked the idols of his family

4. Kaboo escaped the dangers of the forest and arrived at _?_.
   a. a colony of slave traders
   b. a colony of people who set slaves free
   c. a mission station
   d. a seaport

5. How did Kaboo respond when he learned about the true God?

   ____

6. True or False: When Kaboo arrived in the United States, he was surprised to see that many American Christians were more interested in earth than they were in Heaven.

7. Kaboo, who changed his name to Sammy Morris, studied in the United States and wanted to be a missionary, but _?_.
   a. he became a business man instead
   b. he forgot about the God who had helped him
   c. God took him to Heaven
   d. he became a sailor

Number of words: 630 ÷ ____ Minutes reading time = rate ____

Quiz 16
The Bread, Cake, and Candy Man
Page 46

__________ %

__________ wpm

Name ______________________________________

Directions: Circle or write the correct answer.

1. Tachiro Morinaga came to the United States from Japan to _?_.
   - **a.** become a baker
   - **b.** become rich and famous
   - **c.** gain friends
   - **d.** sell his uncle's pottery

2. When he was not successful, Morinaga took a job as a

   ____ .

3. Morinaga was influenced to become a Christian because _?_ .
   - **a.** he went to many church services
   - **b.** his employer and other Christians were so kind to him
   - **c.** he thought it would help him gain money
   - **d.** his employer demanded it

4. True or False: After he became a Christian, Morinaga worked for six years to pay off his business debt.

5. Morinaga worked various places to learn how to _?_.
   - **a.** work on machinery
   - **b.** manufacture toys
   - **c.** make bread, cake, and candy
   - **d.** tailor clothes

6. What nickname did the people of Japan give to Morinaga?
   - **a.** The Chocolate King
   - **b.** Mr. Baker
   - **c.** Mr. Delicious
   - **d.** The Cookie Man

7. Morinaga advertised what Jesus had done for him by putting a Bible verse on

   ____ .

8. Morinaga's story shows that a person can be successful in business _?_.
   - **a.** only if his parents help him get started
   - **b.** if he never lets anyone know he is a Christian
   - **c.** if he has a lot of money to begin with
   - **d.** and have a good Christian testimony too

Number of words: 665 ÷ _____ Minutes reading time = rate _____

Quiz 17
A Bulldog, a Goat, and an Elephant
Page 50

_________ %

_________ wpm

Name ________________________________

Directions: *Circle or write the correct answer.*

1. The Burmese people did not come to the missionary doctor because __?__.
   a. it was too expensive
   b. they were never sick
   c. their ruler did not approve of him
   d. the doctor was not skillful

2. When nobody came for his services, the missionary doctor __?__.
   a. asked the President of the United States for help
   b. asked God why He had sent him to Burma
   c. waited and prayed to God
   d. gave up and returned to his country

3. One day the ruler's servant brought the missionary __?__.
   a. a dog with a blister
   b. a dog with a toothache
   c. a dog with an earache
   d. a mad dog

4. The missionary __?__.
   a. sent the man away
   b. relieved the dog's pain
   c. told him he did not work on animals
   d. decided to return to America

5. The next animals brought to him were

   ____.

6. True or False: As a result of the missionary's treating the Sawbwa's animals, the people would bring only their animals to the missionary for treatment.

7. True or False: As God used even animals to accomplish His purposes, He can also use children.

Number of words: 670 ÷ ____ Minutes reading time = rate ____

Quiz 18
Street Boy
Page 54

__________ %

__________ wpm

Name ______________________________________

Directions: *Circle or write the correct answer.*

1. Samuel was a boy of _?_.
   a. the Philippines
   b. Japan
   c. Russia

2. Where did Sammy live when his mother did not take care of him?

   ____

3. There Sammy learned to _?_.
   a. help people
   b. steal and hide from the police
   c. work

4. What kind of book did the foreign man show the street children _?_.
   a. a wordless book
   b. a Bible
   c. a picture book

5. Fill in the blanks:

   The dark page stood for __________________________.

   The red page stood for Jesus' ____________________that was shed for us.

   The white page stood for a ______________________________.

   The gold page stood for _________________________________.

6. What did the Christian man offer Samuel?
   a. money
   b. a job
   c. a home

7. Circle the letters for the things Samuel received from the man.
   a. food
   b. clothing
   c. lots of toys
   d. a chance to go to school
   e. a chance to learn about Jesus

8. True or False: We can help homeless children by giving to missions who help people like Sammy.

Number of words: 695 ÷ _____ Minutes reading time = rate _____

Quiz 19
When Darkness Falls
Part 1
Page 58

__________ %

__________ wpm

Name ____

Directions: *Circle or write the correct answer.*

1. Mark's parents were missionaries to the Campa people in _?_.
   a. India **c.** Peru
   b. Bolivia **d.** Japan

2. What did the Campa people worship as their god?

   ____

3. The Campa people were fearful at night because _?_.
   a. they often became ill when the temperature dropped at night
   b. they were afraid of attacks from neighboring tribes
   c. wild animals from the jungle attacked the natives at night
   d. their god abandoned them at night

4. Why was the river a dangerous place to swim?
   a. There were rapids.
   b. There were dangerous creatures in it.
   c. It was too deep.
   d. The current was very strong.

5. Why was Mark's friend Vishnu sad?

   ____

6. What time of day did the boys leave the house to go into the jungle?
   a. right after breakfast
   b. mid afternoon
   c. in the evening
   d. midnight

7. True or False: Mark became uneasy about being in the jungle, because his father was not there with his gun.

8. The boys went into the jungle to _?_.
   a. find another monkey for Vishnu
   b. gather flowers for their mothers
   c. pick bananas to eat
   d. swing in the vines

Number of words: 690 ÷ _____ Minutes reading time = rate _____

Quiz 20
When Darkness Falls
Part 2
Page 62

__________ %

__________ wpm

Name ________________________________

Directions: *Circle or write the correct answer.*

1. True or False: Mark and Vishnu had gone into the jungle to collect firewood.

2. Why did Mark become uneasy?
   a. They had food and water for only one more day.
   b. He knew the jungle was a dangerous place.
   c. He was afraid Vishnu would run off and leave him.
   d. He was afraid of the darkness for the same reason Vishnu was.

3. The boys realized they were going in circles when they _?_.
   a. saw a piece of Mark's shirt on a thorn bush
   b. did not come to the edge of the jungle
   c. could not find the trail
   d. recognized a tree they had seen earlier

4. Why was Vishnu terrified when it got dark?
   a. He saw animals' eyes watching him.
   b. He was getting very cold.
   c. He knew he'd be in trouble when he got home.
   d. The sun, his god, was gone.

5. When Mark realized they were lost, he _?_.
   a. began to cry
   b. blamed Vishnu
   c. prayed to God
   d. called for help

6. True or False: Mark sent up a flare to help rescuers find him.

7. When darkness came, where did the boys decide to spend the night?

   ____

Number of words: 695 ÷ _____ Minutes reading time = rate _____

Quiz 21
When Darkness Falls
Part 3
Page 65

__________ %

__________ wpm

Name ____________________________________

Directions: *Circle or write the correct answer.*

1. True or False: Mark told Vishnu that the true God was with them all the time, not just in the daytime.

2. When Vishnu heard wailing in the dark, he believed it was _?_.
   a. a dead person's spirit **c.** a wildcat
   b. a bird **d.** someone lost in the jungle

3. Where did the two eyes the boys saw in the dark come from?

   ____

4. What was the third bright light they saw in the dark?
   a. the headlight from a jeep
   b. the lantern Mark's father was holding
   c. Mark's father's flashlight
   d. light from a hut in the jungle

5. Suddenly Mark and Vishnu heard a deafening noise which turned out to be _?_.
   a. a lion's roar
   b. a gun going off
   c. an animal crashing through the brush
   d. a loud clap of thunder

6. How had Mark's father found the boys?
   a. Hunting dogs led the men to the boys.
   b. He followed the map they always used in the jungle.
   c. Mark's mother told him where to look.
   d. He followed the bits of shirt Mark had dropped.

7. Circle the letters for the things that tell what lessons Mark learned from his experience.
   a. that he has a full-time God
   b. that he can pray to God anytime
   c. that some things aren't important enough to pray about
   d. that his father would be angry if he disobeyed

8. True or False: Even though Vishnu had been terrified, the experience had not really frightened Mark.

Number of words: 820 ÷ _____ Minutes reading time = rate _____

Quiz 22
The Girl of Siberia
Part 1
Page 69

_________ %
_________ wpm

Name ______________________________

Directions: *Circle or write the correct answer.*

1. When she was a young child, Lilia __?__.
   a. could go to church to learn about God
   b. did not care to learn about God
   c. learned about God from her parents and late night radio programs
   d. learned about God from her friends at school

2. In the public schools in the Soviet Union, students were taught that __?__.
   a. there is a God
   b. there is no God
   c. there are many gods
   d. there used to be a god, but he no longer exists

3. True or False: After listening to the Christian radio programs late at night, Lilia came to know and love her parents' Savior.

4. When Lilia's parents took three of their girls out of the public school, __?__.
   a. they were allowed to be taught at home
   b. the mother was imprisoned
   c. the girls were kidnapped and sent to a boarding school far away
   d. the girls were kidnapped and sent to a rich family in America

5. Finally, Peter Vashchenko decided to take his family to a country where they could have __?__.
   a. freedom of religion
   b. freedom of speech
   c. freedom of the press
   d. freedom to teach his children at home

6. When they arrived in Moscow, the Vashchenko family __?__.
   a. was invited to the U.S. embassy
   b. ran into the U.S. embassy without permission
   c. camped outside the U.S. embassy
   d. went to the Russian embassy first

7. Which family member did not make it safely to the U.S. embassy?

   ____

8. How long did the Vashchenko family live in the basement apartment in the U.S. embassy in Moscow?

   ____

Number of words: 705 ÷ _____ Minutes reading time = rate _____

Name ______________________________

Quiz 23
Girl of Siberia
Part 2
Page 73

________ %

________ wpm

Directions: *Circle or write the correct answer.*

1. The Vashchenko family was finally allowed to leave the Soviet Union because _?_.
   a. of the change of laws in their country
   b. of pressure from the U.S. government
   c. they became ill in the embassy
   d. their country got a new leader

2. When the family arrived in the United States, the parents and younger children settled in the state of

   ____.

3. Lilia was amazed when she saw _?_.
   a. how Americans dressed
   b. the tall buildings in the United States
   c. the variety and amount of food in the grocery stores
   d. how beautiful America was

4. What shocked Lilia the most about the United States was _?_.
   a. everyone seemed rich
   b. so many people were educated
   c. in spite of religious freedom, everyone was not a Christian
   d. how friendly everyone was

5. Lilia learned English and finished her high school education, and then enrolled in _?_.
   a. a university
   b. a medical school
   c. a business college
   d. a trade school

6. What is the former Soviet Union now called?

   ____

7. True or False: Lilia's homeland now enjoys a measure of religious freedom.

Number of words: 735 ÷ _____ Minutes reading time = rate _____

Quiz 24
Happy Ending
Page 77

_________ %

_________ wpm

Name ________________________________

Directions: *Circle or write the correct answer.*

1. Junichi was an eight-year-old boy who lived in

   ______________.

2. The kami-shibai man told stories about __?__.
   - **a.** Jesus
   - **b.** history
   - **c.** evil creatures
   - **d.** famous people

3. Junichi had been taught by his family that __?__.
   - **a.** there are many gods
   - **b.** there is only one true God
   - **c.** gods are not important
   - **d.** he was a sinner

4. Junichi felt sad because __?__.
   - **a.** his family was not rich
   - **b.** his family made him stay home always
   - **c.** his father drank rice wine and became drunk
   - **d.** his mother was cruel to him

5. The Christian ladies who showed their pictures told Junichi that __?__.
   - **a.** all gods are the same
   - **b.** he must work his way to Heaven
   - **c.** Jesus could forgive his sins
   - **d.** his father would never stop drinking

6. On his way home, Junichi __?__.
   - **a.** decided he liked the stories about evil creatures better
   - **b.** asked Jesus to forgive his sins
   - **c.** decided not to go back to hear more about Jesus
   - **d.** got hit by a car

7. True or False: The next time Junichi went to hear the stories about Jesus, he barely beat the train across the tracks.

8. For whom did Junichi call when he was suffering in the hospital?

   ____

Number of words: 755 ÷ _____ Minutes reading time = rate _____

Quiz 25
Choco Calls
Part 1
Page 81

__________ %

__________ wpm

Name ______________________________________

Directions: *Circle or write the correct answer.*

1. Choco was a boy of _?_.
   - **a.** Mexico
   - **b.** Bolivia
   - **c.** Vietnam
   - **d.** Peru

2. When Choco saw his father looking sad, he thought _?_.
   - **a.** he was out of money
   - **b.** he was sick
   - **c.** someone was out to harm him
   - **d.** he had done something wrong

3. True or False: Choco was bothered by his father's behavior that morning because his father usually didn't worry about things.

4. Choco decided to help by _?_.
   - **a.** staying home with his mother
   - **b.** going hunting for food for the family
   - **c.** going to the missionary with his father
   - **d.** looking for a rubber tree to tap

5. One of Choco's early morning jobs was to _?_.
   - **a.** build a cooking fire
   - **b.** get water for his mother
   - **c.** pick bananas for breakfast
   - **d.** cook rice for breakfast

6. What happened to Choco when he went into the forest?

   ____

7. Choco remembered a verse the missionary had told them about _?_.
   - **a.** living a good life
   - **b.** being punished
   - **c.** calling upon the Lord
   - **d.** obeying their parents

8. True or False: When Choco could not find his way home, he asked the missionary's God for help.

Number of words: 765 ÷ _____ Minutes reading time = rate _____

Name ______________________________

Quiz 26
Choco Calls
Part 2
Page 85

________ %

________ wpm

Directions: *Circle or write the correct answer.*

1. When Choco realized he was walking in circles, what did he remember that he should do?
   a. call for help
   b. send up a flare
   c. climb a tall tree and look around
   d. use his compass

2. For what did Choco search to help him do this?

   ____

3. The missionary gave Choco the Bible verse, "Whosoever shall

   ____________ upon the name of the Lord shall be

   ______________."

4. Who came to Choco's rescue?
   a. the missionary
   b. his father
   c. the village chief
   d. his best friend

5. True or False: Choco's father did not look sad and worried anymore, because he had become a child of God.

6. What had Choco's father purchased from the missionary?

   ____

7. True or False: Instead of smoking rubber that evening, Choco was going to read the New Testament to his father.

8. Choco learned that it is easy to find your way through the jungle when you have a guide. What can we learn from his experience?
   a. We should ask our friends to guide us through life.
   b. We should follow our heart.
   c. Jesus should be our guide through life since He knows what is best for us.
   d. We should choose our own way through life and always do our best.

Number of words: 770 ÷ ______ Minutes reading time = rate ______

Quiz 27
Marie's Dream
Part 1
Page 88

Name ______________________________

________ %

________ wpm

Directions: *Circle or write the correct answer.*

1. Marie's great desire was to be a

   ______________________________________.

2. Marie lost her leg _?_.
   a. in a car accident
   b. in a storm
   c. from having polio
   d. in an accident on the farm

3. When Marie was a teenager, she was unhappy for a time because _?_.
   a. she forgot about serving God
   b. she was unpopular
   c. she had an artificial leg
   d. her family was poor

4. Marie's joy came back to her when _?_.
   a. she got a job and could earn money
   b. her parents moved off the farm
   c. she realized Jesus had forgiven her sins
   d. she became popular with her friends

5. People thought Marie was foolish to go to China because _?_.
   a. she had an artificial leg
   b. it was dangerous
   c. she could make more money in the United States
   d. people in China did not need Jesus

6. True or False: Marie's parents encouraged her in her plans to go to China.

7. True or False: The mission board finally accepted Marie as a missionary candidate.

8. When it came time to leave America, Marie found it hard to _?_.
   a. leave her comfortable home
   b. say good-bye to her family and friends
   c. leave her land of freedom
   d. leave her life of comfort and ease

Number of words: 760 ÷ _____ Minutes reading time = rate _____

Quiz 28
Marie's Dream Part 2
Page 92

_________ %
_________ wpm

Name ______________________________

Directions: *Circle or write the correct answer.*

1. After Marie's first ocean voyage to China, she decided that she ______________________________ ______________________________.

2. Actually, after that first trip, Marie crossed the ocean by ship __?__.
   a. another time **b.** six more times **c.** nine more times **d.** twelve more times

3. The last lap of that first journey was made __?__.
   a. by plane **b.** by boat **c.** in a sedan chair **d.** on foot

4. The people wanted to get into the rooms of the missionaries because they __?__.
   a. were curious about them
   b. wanted to rob them
   c. wanted to learn English
   d. wanted to hurt them

5. What was Marie's first task in her new place?

   ____

6. The Chinese people blamed the missionaries when disaster struck because they __?__.
   a. did not like Americans
   b. were superstitious
   c. were cruel
   d. needed to blame someone

7. Circle two dangers the missionaries faced in China.
   a. polluted water **b.** bandits **c.** unhealthy food **d.** Japanese bombs

8. True or False: Marie's story shows us that God uses only strong people.

Number of words: 880 ÷ _____ Minutes reading time = rate _____

QUIZ ANSWER KEY

Quiz 1 ***God Was Taking Care of Andre***—p. 2

1. d
2. c
3. d
4. d
5. b
6. False

Quiz 2 ***The Most Important Lesson, Part 1***—p. 5

1. a
2. play with her friend (Teiko San)
3. c
4. d
5. a
6. c

Quiz 3 ***The Most Important Lesson, Part 2***—p. 8

1. c
2. d
3. c
4. b
5. the Christmas party
6. False

Quiz 4 ***The Most Important Lesson, Part 3***—p. 10

1. a
2. c
3. b
4. a
5. True
6. Heaven
7. True

Quiz 5 ***Village Boy of Mexico, Part 1***—p. 13

1. a
2. b
3. False
4. The missionary wife stood while she cooked.
   The missionary wife sat down with her husband while they ate.
   The missionaries closed their eyes before they ate.
5. c
6. language of his people
7. False

Quiz 6 ***Village Boy of Mexico, Part 2***—p. 16

1. Which were the true gods?
2. c
3. a
4. c
5. False
6. True
7. c

Quiz 7 ***A Testing Time, Part 1***—p. 19

1. True
2. False
3. b
4. c
5. b
6. True
7. False

Quiz 8 ***A Testing Time, Part 2***—p. 22

1. c
2. two
3. a
4. False
5. c
6. False
7. b, c

Quiz 9 ***A Testing Time, Part 3***—p. 25

1. c
2. two Russian children
3. b
4. b
5. True
6. False
7. d

Quiz 10 ***Anatole's Adventure***—p. 28

1. True
2. False
3. because he was a Christian
4. b
5. b
6. c
7. d
8. b

Quiz 11 ***Yochi's Front Teeth, Part 1***—p. 31

1. having his teeth sawed off
2. d
3. b
4. b
5. True
6. c
7. a
8. He climbed a tree in the forest.

Quiz 12 ***Yochi's Front Teeth, Part 2***—p. 34

1. c
2. False
3. c
4. Yochi's father
5. b
6. True
7. the skies

Quiz 13 ***Detour to Joy***—p. 37

1. b
2. They both died.
3. d
4. True
5. a
6. They read it.
7. a, c
8. False

Quiz 14 ***The Domino Effect***—p. 40

1. b
2. c
3. d
4. b
5. a
6. Sumiko
7. Mr. Saito
8. many others

Quiz 15 ***Rescued Two Ways***—p. 43
1. b
2. d
3. c
4. b
5. He believed right away.
6. True
7. c

Quiz 16 ***The Bread, Cake, and Candy Man***—p. 46
1. d
2. servant
3. b
4. True
5. c
6. a
7. the top of his delivery car
8. d

Quiz 17 ***A Bulldog, a Goat, and an Elephant***—p. 50
1. c
2. c
3. b
4. b
5. a goat and an elephant
6. False
7. True

Quiz 18 ***Street Boy***—p. 54
1. a
2. on the streets
3. b
4. a
5. sin, blood, clean heart, Heaven
6. c
7. a, b, d, e
8. True

Quiz 19 ***When Darkness Falls, Part 1***—p. 58
1. c
2. the sun
3. d
4. b
5. His monkey had died.
6. b
7. True
8. a

Quiz 20 ***When Darkness Falls, Part 2***—p. 62
1. False
2. b
3. a
4. d
5. c
6. False
7. in a tree

Quiz 21 ***When Darkness Falls, Part 3***—p. 65
1. True
2. a
3. a stalking animal
4. c
5. b
6. d
7. a, b
8. False

Quiz 22 ***Girl of Siberia, Part 1***—p. 69
1. c
2. b
3. True
4. c
5. a
6. b
7. Lilia's brother
8. five years

Quiz 23 ***Girl of Siberia, Part 2***—p. 73
1. b
2. Washington
3. c
4. c
5. a
6. C.I.S. (The Commonwealth of Independent States)
7. True

Quiz 24 ***Happy Ending***—p. 77
1. Japan
2. c
3. a
4. c
5. c
6. b
7. False
8. Iesu (Jesus)

Quiz 25 ***Choco Calls, Part 1***—p. 81
1. b
2. a
3. True
4. d
5. b
6. He got lost.
7. c
8. True

Quiz 26 ***Choco Calls, Part 2***—p. 85
1. a
2. anthorn
3. call, saved
4. b
5. True
6. a New Testament
7. True
8. c

Quiz 27 ***Marie's Dream, Part 1***—p. 88
1. a missionary to China
2. d
3. a
4. c
5. a
6. False
7. True
8. b

Quiz 28 ***Marie's Dream, Part 2***—p. 92
1. never wanted to cross the ocean again
2. c
3. c
4. a
5. to learn the Chinese language
6. b
7. b, d
8. False